Practical
Exercises
for
New CLAIT
2006

Jackie Sherman

Practical Exercises for New CLAIT 2006

PEARSON
Prentice
Hall

Harlow, England • London • New York • Boston • San Francisco • Toronto
Sydney • Tokyo • Singapore • Hong Kong • Seoul • Taipei • New Delhi
Cape Town • Madrid • Mexico City • Amsterdam • Munich • Paris • Milan

Pearson Education Limited
Edinburgh Gate
Harlow
Essex CM20 2JE
England

and Associated Companies throughout the world

Visit us on the World Wide Web at:

www.pearsoned.co.uk

First published 2006

ISBN: 0 13 227727 1
ISBN: 978 0 13 227727 3

British Library Cataloguing-in-Publication Data
A catalogue record for this book is available from the British Library.

Library of Congress Cataloging-in-Publication Data
Sherman, Jackie.
    Practical exercises for new CLAIT 2006/Jackie Sherman.
      p. cm.
    ISBN 0-13-227727-1
      1. Electronic data processing personnel--Certification. 2. Microsoft softeware--Examinations--Study guides. 3. Microsoft Office--Examinations--Study guides. I. Title.

    QA76.3.S46443 2006
    005.3--dc22

                                                              2005053461

10 9 8 7 6 5 4 3 2 1
10 09 08 07 06

Typeset in 10/13pt Stone Serif by 30
Printed and bound in Great Britain by Henry Ling Ltd, Dorchester

The publisher's policy is to use paper manufactured from sustainable forests.

Contents

Introduction

The New CLAIT 2006 qualification, which replaces the former New CLAIT syllabus, is offered by OCR (Oxford, Cambridge and RSA Examinations) and is accepted by most UK employers as evidence that holders have attained a basic level of computer literacy. Most people study the course and take the assessments after attending a school, college or university department, but classes are also held within the community education sector and some distance learning organizations offer the training to people studying at home.

Using This Book

To gain certification in New CLAIT 2006 you will need to master a wide range of skills in order to carry out the specified tasks, and then practise until you are confident you can perform them accurately, without help. But how can you be sure you are ready to take the qualification?

Although there are many books on the market, including *How to Pass New CLAIT*, that will teach you everything you need to know about the various software applications, ***Practical Exercises for New CLAIT 2006*** is the only publication that provides over 170 exercises to enable you to consolidate your knowledge, identify weak areas where the skills have not yet been fully mastered and test your readiness for the assessment.

The book is designed progressively, so that as you work through the exercises you will find they increase in complexity and will help build up your skills step by step. At the beginning of each exercise, you will be told the skills you will need in order to complete them successfully. Each chapter relates to a single New CLAIT 2006 unit and ends with three full assignments to help you prepare for the final assessment. The book also provides examples of finished pieces of work so that you can check that you have carried out the exercises successfully.

Although all the examples have been created using a PC with the Windows 2000 operating system and Microsoft Office 2000 suite of programs, you can complete the exercises using any type of computer or standard software programs. (For Unit 6, you will also need image editing software such as Paint Shop Pro or PhotoShop.)

Using the CD-ROM

In order to complete the assessments, you must be able to access and open files that have been provided. To give you practice in doing this, all the files and images that you will need for the exercises are included on the accompanying disk which you should place in your CD-ROM drive (usually labelled D:).

You can use them in one of three ways, once you are able to save and copy files:

1. If the disk does not open automatically, open My Computer from the desktop and then open the CD-ROM (or open the disk using your own operating system). Open any file and use File – Save As to save a copy onto your hard disk, e.g. into My Documents.

2. Open the CD-ROM, select all the closed files and copy them across into a folder on your computer.

3. Access or insert the text or images directly from the disk whenever you are asked to use them in an exercise, in the same way that you would use files that are on your hard drive (C:) or a floppy disk (A:).

[Note that if you want to *open* the original file that is on the CD-ROM and then amend it and update your work, it must be saved with a new filename as it will be Read-Only and you will not be able to save any changes to the original file.]

About the author

Jackie Sherman has been involved in teaching and assessing IT courses at Further Education colleges since 1996. She also trains staff in an education department and writes courses for distance learning colleges. Her online activities include involvement with the National Tutor Database for LearnDirect and answering IT questions for the YouCanDoIT column for www.laterlife.com. Jackie is the author of several successful IT books.

Acknowledgements

We are grateful to the following for permission to reproduce copyright material:

Exercise 8.13a answer: Pearson Education homepage from http://www.pearsoned.com/index.htm. Pearson Education, Inc. Reprinted by permission of Pearson Education, Inc., Upper Saddle River, New Jersey; Exercises 8.13a, 8.13b, 8.13c, 8.14, 8.15a, 8.15b, 8.18b, 8.18c, 8.19b and 8.20a answers: Screenshot frames reprinted by permission from Microsoft Corporation; Exercise 8.13b answer: Screenshot of search results from google.com:http://www.google.co.uk/search?hl=en&q=Poisonous+plants &btnG=Google. Google is a trademark of Google, Inc. Reprinted by permission of Google, Inc.; Exercise 8.13c answer: Screenshot from the Guide to Poisonous Plants website: http://www.vth. colostate.edu/poisonous_ plants/report/plant_report2.cfm. Reprinted by permission of A. P. Knight, Department of Clinical Sciences, Colorado State University; Exercise 8.14 answer: Screenshot from the Rail Europe website: http://www.railerope. com/us/rail/eurostar/. Reprinted by permission of Rail Europe Group; Exercise 8.15a answer: Screenshot of search results from ebay.com:http://musical-instruments.listings.ebay.co.uk/Keyboard-Piano_W0QQfrom ZR4QQscategoryZ16220QQsalicZ3. These materials have been reproduced with the permission of eBay Inc. Copyright © eBay Inc. All rights reserved; Exercise 8.15b answer: Screenshot from the Horniman Museum website:http://www.horniman.ac.uk/collections/musical.php. Reprinted by permission of The Horniman Museum, London; Exercises 8.17a and 8.17b answers: Screenshots from the REACH website: http://www.reach-online.org.uk. Reprinted by permission of REACH Volunteering; Exercise 8.18b answer: Screenshot from the Oxford Brookes University website: https://www.brookes.ac.uk/hon_grads/1996/graduates/sallis_j. Reprinted by permission of Oxford Brookes University and Joan Sallis; Exercise 8.18c answer: Screenshot from the Governornet website: http://www.

governornet.co.uk. Crown copyright material is reproduced under Class Licence Number CO1W0000039 with the permission of the Controller of HMSO and the Queen's Printer for Scotland; Exercise 8.19c answer: Screenshot from the LearnDirect website: http://catalogue.learndirect.co.uk/courses/100972EH017/?view= Ecommerce. Reprinted by permission of Ufi Ltd.; Exercise 8.20b answer: courtesy of The Tea Council Ltd.

In some instances we have been unable to trace the owners of copyright material, and we would appreciate any information that would enable us to do so.

File management and e-document production

This core unit will test your skills in managing files and word processing documents. You will be asked to gain access to data using a login and/or password, create folders in which to store your work, create and save documents, use word processing software to enter text and numbers and then print out your work. You will also need to know how to use a range of facilities that will enable you to format text, change page layouts, add tables, borders and numbered lists and move or replace entries.

EXERCISES 1 AND 2

Test your ability to:

- Gain access to data using a login and/or password
- Create and name folders
- Rename files and folders
- Move files
- Copy files
- Delete files and folders

Assessment Objectives: 1a, 2a, 2b, 2c, 2d and 2e

Exercise 1

1. Switch on the computer.

2. Login using your login/username and password.

3. Locate and rename the folder *Christmas* so that it is now named *Xmas*.

4. In the folder, make a new sub-folder named *Parties*.

5. Copy the text file *games* into the *Parties* folder.

6. Move the text file *holly* from the *files* folder into the *Parties* folder.

7. Delete the *files* folder and its contents.

Answer 1a at step 4

Answer 1b at step 6

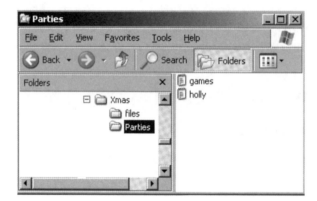

Exercise 2 1. Locate the folder *Sports* and rename it *Ball games*.

2. In the folder, make a new sub-folder named *Golf*.

3. Copy the text file *Rules* into the *Golf* folder.

4. Move the text file *Clothing* from the *Tennis* folder into the *Golf* folder.

5. Delete the file *Davis Cup* in the *Tennis* folder.

Answer 2a at step 2

Answer 2b at step 4

EXERCISES 3 AND 4

Test your ability to:

- Create a new document
- Save documents
- Print documents
- Produce printed evidence of folder contents
- Close files

Assessment Objectives: 1b, 1d and 1e

Exercise 3   1.   Locate the folder *Music* and rename it *Bands*.

2.   In the folder, make a new sub-folder named *Guitarists*.

3.   Copy the text file *Clapton* into the *Guitarists* folder.

4.   Move the text file *Segovia* from the *Drums* folder into the *Guitarists* folder.

5.   Delete the image file *Instrument* in the *Drums* folder.

6.   Using your word processing application:

a) Create a new document.

b) Take a screen print of the folder called *Bands* showing its contents.

c) Take a screen print of the sub-folder *Guitarists* showing its contents.

7.   Save the file(s) containing the screen prints into the *Bands* folder.

8.   Print the file(s) containing the screen prints. Make sure that all the contents of the folder and the sub-folder are clearly visible on the print(s).

9.   Close any open files.

Answer 3a

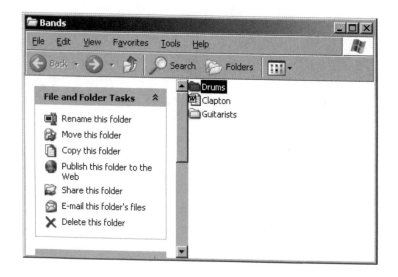

Answer 3b

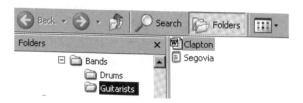

Exercise 4   1.   Locate the folder *Recipes* and rename it *Food*.

2.   In the folder, make a new sub-folder named *Puddings*.

3.   Copy the text file *Cake* into the *Puddings* folder.

4.   Move the text file *Eclairs* from the *Meat* folder into the *Puddings* folder.

5.   Delete the folder *Meat* and its contents.

6.   Using your word processing application:

   a) Create a new document.

   b) Take a screen print of the folder called *Food* showing its contents.

   c) Take a screen print of the sub-folder *Puddings* showing its contents.

7.   Save the screen print(s) into the *Puddings* sub-folder.

8. Print the file(s) containing the screen prints. Make sure that all the contents of the folder and the sub-folder are clearly visible on the print(s).

9. Close any open files.

Answer 4a

Answer 4b

EXERCISES 5, 6 AND 7

Test your ability to:

◆ Enter text, numbers and symbols

◆ Understand the use of proof-reading and spell checkers

Assessment Objective: 3d

Exercise 5 1. Start a new document.

2. Type the heading: Poem.

3. Leave a blank line and then type the first line of any poem, nursery rhyme, Christmas carol or other song (or copy the text in the answer).

4. Type the rest of the first verse, starting a new line for each line of the song.

5. Save the file with the name of the poem, e.g. *The Fox*.

6. Leave a clear line space and then type your name and the date.

7. Check the document and correct any errors.

8. Save the amended document with the original filename.

9. Print a copy and then close the file.

Answer   Poem

I know my way around the glade, my red fur
Will show through the plants and trees,
My snout will pick up the invisible presence
Of the beautiful birds and bees.

My Name 1/4/06

Exercise 6 1. Start a new document.

2. Enter the following:

She asked: 'Is the ticket 20% off?'

3. Save the document with the filename *Ticket*.

4. Insert a clear line space and type:

He said: 'No. Pay Harry's dad £350 now!'

5. Proof read and correct any mistakes.

6. Save the amended document with the filename *Harry*.

7. Print a copy of the document.

8. Close the file.

Exercise 7 1. Start a new document.

2. Enter the heading: Apple Crumble.

3. Now type the following:

Ingredients: 1lb cooking apples – peeled and chopped; 4 oz plain flour; 2 oz marg; 3 oz sugar.

Method: Rub the marg into the flour and then stir in the sugar. Place the chopped apples in a bowl, sprinkle on the crumble mixture and bake for 30 mins at 180 degrees.

4. Proof read and correct any mistakes.

5. Save the file as *Apple Crumble*.

6. Now add the following as a final paragraph:

    You can also make this dessert by replacing the apples with stoned plums.

7. Save the amended document as *Plum Crumble*.

8. Print a copy.

9. Close the file.

Answer

```
Apple Crumble

Ingredients:  1lb cooking apples - peeled and chopped; 4
oz plain flour; 2 oz marg; 3 oz sugar.

Method:  Rub the marg into the flour and then stir in the
sugar.  Place the chopped apples in a bowl, sprinkle on
the crumble mixture and bake for 30 mins at 180 degrees.

You can also make this dessert by replacing the apples
with stoned plums.
```

EXERCISES 8, 9 AND 10

Test your ability to:

◗ Open an existing document

◗ Set page orientation

◗ Set margins

Assessment Objectives: 1c, 3a and 3b

Exercise 8 1. Open the file *Plum Crumble* created earlier.

2. Change to landscape orientation.

3. Set the left and right page margins to 4 cm.

4. Save as *Plum Crumble amended*.

5. Close the file.

Apple Crumble

Ingredients: 1lb cooking apples – peeled and chopped; 4 oz plain flour; 2 oz marg; 3 oz sugar.

Method: Rub the marg into the flour and then stir in the sugar. Place the chopped apples in a bowl, sprinkle on the crumble mixture and bake for 30 mins at 180 degrees.

You can also make this dessert by replacing the apples with stoned plums.

Exercise 9 1. Start a new document.

2. Type the following: **Men's Weight**.

3. Leave a few lines and then enter the following data:

   For height: 5ft 9"
   Underweight: under 135 lb
   Normal weight: from 135–168 lb
   Overweight: from 168–202 lb
   Obese: 202+lb

4. Save the document with the filename *Weight*.

5. Print one copy of the document.

6. Close the file.

7. Re-open *Weight* and change the page orientation to landscape.

8. Increase the right-hand margin by 2 cm.

9. Set the left-hand margin to 5 cm.

10. Print a copy of the amended document.

11. Save as *Weight – landscape*.

12. Close the file.

Answer

```
Men's Weight

For height: 5ft 9"
Underweight: under 135lb
Normal weight: from 135 - 168lb
Overweight: from 168 - 202lb
Obese: 202+lb
```

Exercise 10 1. Start a new document in landscape orientation.

2. Type the following: SUMS.

3. Leave a clear line space and then enter the following data with each sum on a new line:

   16 + 20 = 36
   20% of £50 = £10
   1/10 of 75 = 7.5
   3 cars @ £12,000 each = £36,000

4. Save the document with the filename *Maths*.

5. Increase the top and bottom margins to 6 cm.

6. Save these changes.

7. Print one copy of the document.

8. Close the file.

EXERCISES 11, 12 AND 13

Test your ability to:

♦ Set font type

♦ Set font size

♦ Emphasize text

Assessment Objectives: 4a, 4b and 4c

Exercise 11 1. Open the file *Weight*.

2. A few lines below the end of the text, add the following:

   20% rise in body weight – 86% greater risk of heart disease. Leaflets from janice@health.com

3. [Note that you may find the e-mail address janice@health.com underlined and coloured automatically.]

4. Change the title font so that it is different from the rest of the text.

5. Increase the title font size to 16.

6. Emphasize the last paragraph only by applying an italic emphasis.

7. Save these changes and print one copy of the document.

8. Close the file.

Answer

```
Men's Weight

For height: 5ft 9"
Underweight: under 135lb
Normal weight: from 135 – 168lb
Overweight: from 168 – 202lb
Obese: 202+lb

20% rise in body weight – 86% greater risk of heart disease. Leaflets from
janice@health.com
```

Exercise 12 1. Start a new document and type the following heading:

   British Birds

2. Leave a clear line space and then type the following paragraph:

   A recent survey of neighbourhood birds showed that the commonest bird in Britain is still the sparrow, although there are far fewer than there were ten years ago. Other neighbourhood birds that are also still found in large numbers include starlings, blackbirds and blue tits.

3. Check and correct any errors and then save the document with the file-name *Birds*.

4. Underline the title and make it bold.

5. Select the main text and apply a Courier font size 10.

6. Save these changes, print a copy and then close the file.

Answer

British Birds

A recent survey of neighbourhood birds showed that the commonest bird
in Britain is still the sparrow, although there are far fewer than
there were ten years ago. Other neighbourhood birds that are also
still found in large numbers include starlings, blackbirds and blue
tits.

Exercise 13 1. Start a new document and type the following text:

FLYING SAFELY

In recent months, concern has been expressed about developing deep vein thrombosis (DVT) on long flights. It is due to the production of blood clots and occurs when passengers sit for long periods in cramped conditions.

Although DVTs can be fatal, there are many simple precautions that can be taken to reduce the risk. For example, passengers should make sure that, if they are on flights lasting for more than 3 hours, they get out of their seats and walk around regularly; drink plenty of water; avoid alcohol, coffee and tea; and perform leg-stretching exercises while seated.

2. Check the document, correct any errors and then save as *Flying*.

3. Set the left and right margins to 3.75 cm.

4. Format the main text to Times New Roman font, size 14.

5. Underline the title and increase the font size to 16.

6. Save these changes to update the document.

7. Print a copy of the document.

8. Close the file.

Answer

FLYING SAFELY

In recent months, concern has been expressed about developing
deep vein thrombosis (DVT) on long flights. It is due to the
production of blood clots and occurs when passengers sit for
long periods in cramped conditions.

Although DVTs can be fatal, there are many simple precautions
that can be taken to reduce the risk. For example, passengers
should make sure that, if they are on flights lasting for more than
3 hours, they get out of their seats and walk around regularly;
drink plenty of water; avoid alcohol, coffee and tea; and perform
leg-stretching exercises while seated.

Test your ability to:

◗ Set text alignment

◗ Insert text

◗ Delete text

Assessment Objectives: 3c, 4e and 4g

Exercise 14   1.   Start a new document and type the following:

Careful Drivers

Fatigue is one of the major causes of accidents on motorways. Fatigue reduces the ability of a driver to take in and process information and so reaction time is slower as a result. Fatigue is most likely in conditions which are unchanging – for example driving at night or in fog or for long periods in low density traffic.

The ultimate loss in alertness is falling asleep at the wheel, and it does not depend on fatigue from driving alone. If you have had a long or stressful day, you are much more at risk from fatigue during a journey.

2.   Check for errors and then save the document as *Tiredness*.

3.   In the second paragraph, add the following phrase after long or stressful day:

or you slept badly the night before

4.   Delete the following words in the first paragraph:

or in fog

5.   Centre the heading.

6.   Fully justify the main text.

7.   Change the look of the main text – apply a different font, change the font size or add emphasis. Make sure it is still clearly legible.

8.   Save these changes to update the document and then close the file.

1

Careful Drivers

Fatigue is one of the major causes of accidents on motorways. Fatigue reduces the ability of a driver to take in and process information and so reaction time is slower as a result. Fatigue is most likely in conditions which are unchanging – for example driving at night or for long periods in low density traffic.

The ultimate loss in alertness is falling asleep at the wheel, and it does not depend on fatigue from driving alone. If you have had a long or stressful day or you slept badly the night before, you are much more at risk from fatigue during a journey.

Exercise 15
1. Start a new document and type the following heading, right aligned:

   Entertaining Children

2. Now add the following paragraphs, left aligned:

   The school holidays can be a demanding time for parents, trying to find things their children would like to do. Fortunately, Britain is crammed with exciting and interesting places to visit and many of these are relatively cheap as well.

   When the weather is fine, there is nothing more relaxing than a day out on a steam railway or lazy boat trip down the river, and with older children taking out a rowing boat can be great fun, especially if you make sure you have a picnic hamper with you. Other places that are educational as well as interesting include zoos and farms which usually offer cafés and adventure play areas as well as rides, petting parks, nature trails and a wide range of animals or equipment to see and read about.

3. Check for errors and save as *Children*.

4. Add the following sentence in the first paragraph after would like to do., taking care with the spacing:

   It is particularly hard if you do not have a great deal of money or your own car.

5. Delete the words as well as interesting in the second paragraph.

6. Fully justify the second paragraph only.

7. Apply Arial font size 11 to the first paragraph only.

8. Make the title bold.

9. Save these changes to update the document and then close the file.

Answer

Entertaining Children

The school holidays can be a demanding time for parents, trying to find things their children would like to do. It is particularly hard if you do not have a great deal of money or your own car. Fortunately, Britain is crammed with exciting and interesting places to visit and many of these are relatively cheap as well.

When the weather is fine, there is nothing more relaxing than a day out on a steam railway or lazy boat trip down the river, and with older children taking out a rowing boat can be great fun, especially if you make sure you have a picnic hamper with you. Other places that are educational include zoos and farms which usually offer cafés and adventure play areas as well as rides, petting parks, nature trails and a wide range of animals or equipment to see and read about.

Exercise 16

1. Open the file *AutoText* from the CD.

2. Add the following words after entire entry in the first paragraph:

   by dragging with your mouse

3. Delete the words where you can use it over and over again in the second paragraph.

4. Centre the heading and make it bold, font size 18.

5. Justify the main text and apply a different font.

6. Set the left and right margins to 4 cm.

7. Save these changes to update the document and then close the file.

Answer

AutoText

A quick and simple way to add the same words to different word processed documents is to use AutoText. When you first type the text, such as your home address, you can select the entire entry by dragging with your mouse and then open the Insert menu. Click on the option labelled AutoText and select New to open a small window.

If you now type an abbreviation for your selected words, such as Add, into the window you can save the address into your computer. Next time you need to type your address, type the abbreviation and then press the key labelled F3 at the top of your keyboard. The full address will now appear on the page.

1

Test your ability to:

♦ Insert a paragraph break

♦ Move text

♦ Set line spacing

Assessment Objectives: 4d, 4f and 4h

Exercise 17 1. Open the file *Home Baking* from the CD.

2. Insert a paragraph break and clear line space after the words:

   such an outlay.

3. Move the sentence:

   Instead, they buy bread-making machines

   found at the start of the second paragraph so that it becomes the last sentence of the *first* paragraph.

4. Double line space the final paragraph only.

5. Save these changes and print a copy before closing the file.

Answer

```
Home Baking

There is nothing quite like the smell of new bread to
excite the taste buds, and yet very few people take the
time or trouble to bake their own loaves.  This is most
surprising as home baking is so easy and quick to do.
Instead, they buy bread-making machines.

Although machines certainly produce good results, there
is no need for such an outlay.

All that is required is strong bread flour, salt,
sugar, warm water, instant yeast and a large bowl.  Oh,
and of course about ten minutes to mix all the
ingredients together plus a hot oven for baking.

There are a wide variety of breads that you can make,

which vary depending on the type of flour and extra

ingredients such as milk, vegetables or seeds that you

add.
```

Exercise 18   1.   Start a new document and type the following text:

Earache

It is probably no surprise to learn that more days off work are blamed on earache than any other illness or injury aside from the common cold.

Earache has no barriers – it is suffered by people across nationalities, professions, the sexes and age groups, and although some people treat it as a joke, sufferers know that it is a most unpleasant and stressful disability. We therefore spend a fortune seeking a cure, although this can often be in our own hands at a considerably cheaper cost than buying professional advice or medication.

2.   Check for errors and then save the document as *Days off*.

3.   Leave a few lines and type your name and today's date.

4.   Print one copy of your document.

5.   Now add the following phrase in the second paragraph after stressful disability:

that we would do almost anything to sort out

6.   Delete the following phrase from the last sentence:

professional advice or

7.   Move the last sentence beginning We therefore spend so that it becomes the last sentence in the *first* paragraph.

8.   Insert a paragraph break and clear line space after the words common cold in the first paragraph.

9.   Set the first paragraph in 1.5 line spacing.

10.   Update the document and print a second copy showing the changes you have made.

11.   Close the document.

Answer

Earache

It is probably no surprise to learn that more days off
work are blamed on earache than any other illness or
injury aside from the common cold.

We therefore spend a fortune seeking a cure, although
this can often be in our own hands at a considerably
cheaper cost than buying medication.

Earache has no barriers – it is suffered by people
across nationalities, professions, the sexes and age
groups, and although some people treat it as a joke,
sufferers know that it is a most unpleasant and
stressful disability that we would do almost anything
to sort out.

EXERCISES 19 AND 20

Test your ability to:

◗ Insert tables

◗ Apply borders and shading

Assessment Objectives: 3e and 3f

Exercise 19 1. Open the file *Birds*.

2. Add the following text as the second paragraph:

When you go into the neighbourhood to study birds, make sure you take with you binoculars and a booklet such as the RSPB's guide to British birds to help you identify the birds you see. Sometimes, birds such as house sparrows and hedge sparrows can be quite hard to distinguish and it is always good to record species accurately if you can.

3. Insert a paragraph break and a clear line space at the end of this paragraph and then create a table with 3 columns and 5 rows.

4. Insert the following data:

Common Name	Latin Name	Preferences
Greenfinch	Chloris chloris	Seeds and berries
Starling	Sturnus vulgaris	Animal and vegetable
House sparrow	Passer domesticus	Corn, seeds and insects
Magpie	Pica pica	Small mammals and birds

5. Make sure all data is fully displayed and the borders will be visible on a printout.

6. Format the column headings Common Name, Latin Name and Preferences to bold.

7. Centre the data in the Preferences column only.

8. Right-align the two column headings Latin Name and Preferences.

9. Save the amended file as *British Birds* and print a copy before closing.

Answer

British Birds

A recent survey of neighbourhood birds showed that the commonest bird in Britain is still the sparrow, although there are far fewer than there were ten years ago. Other neighbourhood birds that are also still found in large numbers include starlings, blackbirds and blue tits.

When you go into the neighbourhood to study birds, make sure you take with you binoculars and a booklet such as the RSPB's guide to British birds to help you identify the birds you see. Sometimes, birds such as house sparrows and hedge sparrows can be quite hard to distinguish and it is always good to record species accurately if you can.

Common Name	Latin Name	Preferences
Greenfinch	Chloris chloris	Seeds and berries
Starling	Sturnus vulgaris	Animal and vegetable
House sparrow	Passer domesticus	Corn, seeds and insects
Magpie	Pica pica	Small mammals and birds

Exercise 20

1. Open the file *Home Baking*.

2. Insert a paragraph break and clear line space after the words:

   plus a hot oven for baking

   at the end of the 3rd paragraph.

3. Create a table that has 2 columns and 5 rows.

4. Enter the following data:

Ingredients for Seed Bread	**Quantity**
Strong white flour	1.5 lb
Yeast	1 packet
Poppy seeds	2 tbs
Caraway seeds	1 pinch

5. Right-align the column heading Quantity and all entries in that column only.

6. Format the column headings Ingredients for Seed Bread and Quantity to bold.

7. Format the entries in the Ingredients column to italic.

8. Shade the Caraway seeds entry only so that it appears against a light grey background.

9. Remove the borders of the table so they do not appear on any printout.

10. Save these changes to update the file and print one copy before closing.

Answer

```
Home Baking

There is nothing quite like the smell of new bread to
excite the taste buds, and yet very few people take the
time or trouble to bake their own loaves.    This is most
surprising as home baking is so easy and quick to do.
Instead, they buy bread-making machines.

Although machines certainly produce good results, there
is no need for such an outlay.

All that is required is strong bread flour, salt,
sugar, warm water, instant yeast and a large bowl.    Oh,
and of course about ten minutes to mix all the
ingredients together plus a hot oven for baking.
```

```
Ingredients for Seed Bread        Quantity
Strong white flour                  1.5lb
Yeast                              1 packet
Poppy seeds                          2 tbs
Caraway seeds                      1 pinch

There are a wide variety of breads that you can make,

which vary depending on the type of flour and extra

ingredients such as milk, vegetables or seeds that you

add.
```

EXERCISES 21 AND 22

Test your ability to:

◗ Insert headers and footers

◗ Use bullets or numbering

◗ Replace text

Assessment Objectives: 3g, 3h and 4i

Exercise 21

1. Open the file *British Birds*.

2. Add the words Garden Birds as a header.

3. Add automatic page numbers as a footer.

4. Leave a clear line space below the table and add the following text as a list:

   Encourage birds with seeds and berries.
   Build a bird table.
   Set up nesting boxes.

5. Replace the word neighbourhood with garden wherever it occurs in the text (3 times).

6. Apply numbers to the list items.

7. Save these changes and then close the document.

1

Garden Birds

British Birds

A recent survey of garden birds showed that the commonest bird in
Britain is still the sparrow, although there are far fewer than there
were ten years ago. Other garden birds that are also still found in
large numbers include starlings, blackbirds and blue tits.

When you go into the garden to study birds, make sure you
take with you binoculars and a booklet such as the RSPB's
guide to British birds to help you identify the birds you
see. Sometimes, birds such as house sparrows and hedge
sparrows can be quite hard to distinguish and it is
always good to record species accurately if you can.

Common Name	Latin Name	Preferences
Greenfinch	Chloris chloris	Seeds and berries
Starling	Sturnus vulgaris	Animal and vegetable
House sparrow	Passer domesticus	Corn, seeds and insects
Magpie	Pica pica	Small mammals and birds

1. Encourage birds with seeds and berries.
2. Build a bird table.
3. Set up nesting boxes.

Exercise 22

1. Open the file *Earache*.

2. Replace the word **earache** with **backache** wherever it occurs in the text (3 times), maintaining initial capitals where required.

3. Insert a paragraph break and clear line space after the words **buying medication** and then add the following as a new paragraph:

   There are a variety of treatments including:
   Lotions
   Osteopathy
   Physiotherapy
   More supportive seating

4. Save the file as *Backache* and print a copy.

5. Add the automatic file name as a header and automatic date as a footer.

6. Apply bullets to the list of four treatments.

7. Save these changes and print a copy of the document before closing.

Answer

```
Backache

Backache

It is probably no surprise to learn that more days off
work are blamed on backache than any other illness or
injury aside from the common cold.

We therefore spend a fortune seeking a cure, although
this can often be in our own hands at a considerably
cheaper cost than buying medication.

There are a variety of treatments including:
    •  Lotions
    •  Osteopathy
    •  Physiotherapy
    •  More supportive seating

Backache has no barriers - it is suffered by people
across nationalities, professions, the sexes and age
groups, and although some people treat it as a joke,
sufferers know that it is a most unpleasant and
stressful disability that we would do almost anything
to sort out.
```

EXERCISES 23 AND 24

Test your ability to:

◗ Indent text

◗ Use word count

Assessment Objectives: 3i and 3j

Exercise 23 1. Open the file *Children*.

2. Insert a paragraph break and clear line space after the words picnic hamper with you.

3. Indent the line beginning Other places from the left margin.

4. Using the software facilities, carry out a word count in the file.

5. Enter the number of words at the end of the document.

6. Save these changes and close the file.

Answer

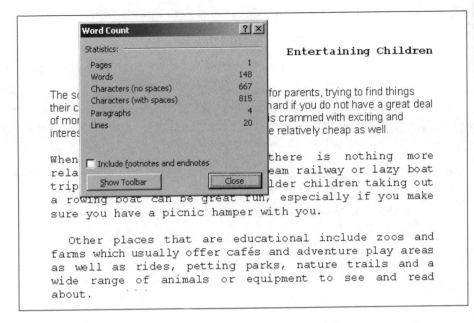

Word Count

Statistics:

Pages	1
Words	148
Characters (no spaces)	667
Characters (with spaces)	815
Paragraphs	4
Lines	20

☐ Include footnotes and endnotes

Show Toolbar   Close

Entertaining Children

The s[...] for parents, trying to find things
their c[...] hard if you do not have a great deal
of mor[...] is crammed with exciting and
interes[...] e relatively cheap as well.

When [...] there is nothing more
rela[...] eam railway or lazy boat
trip[...] lder children taking out
a rowing boat can be great fun, especially if you make
sure you have a picnic hamper with you.

Other places that are educational include zoos and
farms which usually offer cafés and adventure play areas
as well as rides, petting parks, nature trails and a
wide range of animals or equipment to see and read
about. . . .

Exercise 24

1. Start a new document and type the following text:

   Printing

   There are two different types of printer that you might come across at work: laser and inkjet. It has always been the case that laser printers are quite expensive, but the long life of their toner cartridges and speed of printing have made them a popular choice for most text documents.

   Makes of printer include:
   Hewlett Packard
   Canon
   Epson

   Inkjet printers are the normal choice for printing at work in colour. The printers are far cheaper, with some being offered at under £50. Many manufacturers produce machines that have separate containers for the different colours of ink. This means that, if you use a great deal of red for example, you can replace the red cartridge and not have to replace any of the others.

2. Save the file as *Printing*.

3. Apply bullets to the list items: Hewlett Packard, Canon and Epson.

4. Format the heading to Times New Roman, bold, font size 14.

5. Format the main text to Arial font size 12.

6. Increase the left margin by 2 cm.

7. Add a footer that shows the automatic file name and date.

8. Indent the text **Makes of printer include** from the left margin.

9. Fully justify the main text.

10. Insert a paragraph break and clear line space after the words **at work in colour**.

11. Move the sentence beginning **It has always been the case** from the first paragraph so that it becomes the second sentence in the 3rd paragraph after the words **at work in colour**.

12. Use your software facilities to carry out a word count and type the result at the end of the document.

13. Save these changes and close the file.

Answer

Printing

There are two different types of printer that you might come across at work: laser and inkjet.

Makes of printer include:
- Hewlett Packard
- Canon
- Epson

Inkjet printers are the normal choice for printing at work in colour. It has always been the case that laser printers are quite expensive, but the long life of their toner cartridges and speed of printing have made them a popular choice for most text documents.

The printers are far cheaper, with some being offered at under £50. Many manufacturers produce machines that have separate containers for the different colours of ink. This means that, if you use a great deal of red for example, you can replace the red cartridge and not have to replace any of the others.

129

FULL ASSIGNMENTS – FILE MANAGEMENT AND E-DOCUMENT PRODUCTION

Exercise 25

Task 1

1. Log in using your username and/or password.

2. Organize your files and folders as follows:

   a) Locate the folder *Science* and rename it *Research*.

   b) In this folder, create a sub-folder named *Questions*.

3. Copy the text file *Projects* into the folder *Questions*.

4. Move the text file *Funding* from the folder *Departments* into the folder *Questions*.

5. Delete the folder *Departments*, including its contents.

6. Take a screen print as evidence of the folder called *Research* and the contents of this folder.

7. Take a screen print of the sub-folder *Questions* and the contents of this folder.

8. In the header of the page displaying the screen print(s), type your name and insert the automatic page number.

9. Save the file(s) containing the screen prints somewhere in your filing system.

10. Print a copy of your screen prints, ensuring all folder contents are fully displayed.

Task 2

11. Open your word processing application and create a new document.

12. Set the page to landscape orientation.

13. Set the left margin to 5 cm.

14. Set the font to Arial.

15. Set the font size to 14.

16. Enter the following text in single line spacing:

Pharaohs

The rulers of Ancient Egypt were called Pharaohs. The name comes from the Egyptian word 'per-ao' which means royal palace, and like our royal family the rulers could be either men or women.

Each family of pharaohs was grouped into a dynasty and there were 31 dynasties covering a period of around 3,000 years. Of the many rulers during that time, some of the most famous were Khufu, Tutankhamen and Hatshepsut.

When a pharaoh died, the body was buried in a 4-sided, triangular tomb known as a pyramid. One of the largest pyramids was built for Khufu and was made of more than two million limestone blocks.

17. Check and correct any errors.

18. Fully justify the main text.

19. Add your name as a header and the automatic date as a footer.

20. Save the file as *Pharaohs* into the folder *Questions*.

21. Close the file.

Task 3

22. Open the file saved as *Pharaohs*.

23. A table needs to be inserted after the second paragraph ending Tutankhamen and Hatshepsut. Insert a paragraph break and clear line space and create a table with 3 columns and 5 rows.

24. Enter the data below into the table:

God	Watched over	Features
Horus the Hawk	Pharaohs	Special protector
Bes	Homes	Drove away evil
Ra	Sun	Took different forms
Khnum	River Nile	Potter

25. Format the column headings God, Watched over and Features to bold, font size 16.

26. Centre the data in the column headed Watched over.

27. Ensure the table borders will be visible on a printout.

28. Save the file and print one copy before closing.

Task 4

29. Open the file provided named *Surveying* that is in the *Research* folder.

30. Save it with the new name *Questionnaire* into the *Questions* folder.

31. Replace the word questionnaires with the word surveys wherever it occurs in the text (4 times).

32. Delete the last sentence of the first paragraph beginning Yet how many of us.

33. Move the sentence It is harder to organize really good surveys than you might imagine from the end of the second paragraph so that it becomes the final sentence of the final paragraph.

34. Insert the words when carrying out a survey in the last paragraph, after Youngman concluded that.

35. Apply numbering to the list of 7 types of question.

36. Indent the final paragraph from the left margin.

37. Double space the first paragraph only.

38. Add your name, the automatic date and the automatic filename in the footer.

39. Carry out a word count and enter the figure at the end of the document at least 2 lines below the text.

40. Save the file and print 1 copy.

41. Close all files.

Answer 25a

Answer 25b

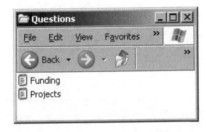

Answer 25c

My Name

Pharaohs

The rulers of Ancient Egypt were called Pharaohs. The name comes from the Egyptian word 'per-ao' which means royal palace, and like our royal family the rulers could be either men or women.

Each family of pharaohs was grouped into a dynasty and there were 31 dynasties covering a period of around 3,000 years. Of the many rulers during that time, some of the most famous were Khufu, Tutankhamen and Hatshepsut.

God	Watched over	Features
Horus the Hawk	Pharaohs	Special protector
Bes	Homes	Drove away evil
Ra	Sun	Took different forms
Khnum	River Nile	Potter

When a pharaoh died, the body was buried in a 4-sided, triangular tomb known as a pyramid. One of the largest pyramids was built for Khufu and was made of more than two million limestone blocks.

```
Surveying the Public

Surveys are used extensively in order to discover what

the general public thinks about the various issues of the

day.  They may be used to discover our political views,

what leisure facilities we want locally or even the type

of breakfast cereal we prefer to eat.


As Oppenheim once wrote, the world is full of well-
meaning people who believe that anyone who can write
plain English and has a modicum of common sense can
produce good surveys, but he then went on to explain that
these virtues are not enough.

Youngman concluded that when carrying out a survey there
are 7 different types of question that can be asked:
   1. verbal
   2. list
   3. category
   4. ranking
   5. scale
   6. quantity
   7. grid

People who organize surveys need to take care when
selecting the type of questions to ask, in actually
wording the question and in the design, piloting,
distribution and return of their forms. It is harder to
organize really good surveys than you might imagine.


171
```

Exercise 26

Task 1

1. Log in using a username and/or password.

2. Locate the folder *Colleges* and rename it *Courses*.

3. In this folder, create a new sub-folder named *Daytime*.

4. Copy the text file provided called *Yoga* to the new folder *Daytime*.

5. Move the text file provided called *Computing* from the folder *Evening* into the folder *Daytime*.

6. Delete the folder *Evening* and all its contents.

7. Take a screen print of the folder *Courses* showing its contents.

8. Take a screen print of the folder *Daytime* showing its contents.

9. In the footer of the file(s) showing the screen prints, add your name and the automatic date.

10. Save the screen prints into the folder *Courses*.

11. Print a copy of your screen prints, ensuring all folder contents are fully displayed.

Task 2

12. Start a new document.

13. Set the page orientation to portrait.

14. Set the left and right margins to 3 cm and the top and bottom margins to 3.5 cm.

15. Type the following text:

    Relaxation Workshop

    Come along to Chesney Town Hall on Thursday, 23 August to learn how to relax. You will be shown the top tips for staying stress-free in our busy modern world and will be provided with simple exercises you can perform at work, when watching TV or even as you wash up!

    Your teacher will be the television celebrity Keep Fit guru Madeleine Switchback.

    The workshop starts at 6.00 p.m. and will finish at 9.00 p.m. Soft drinks are included.

16. Apply Times New Roman font size 11 to the entire document.

17. Double space the main text.

18. Right-align the last sentence.

19. Add your name as a footer and the automatic date and automatic file-name as a header.

20. Check for errors and then save as *Relax* into the *Courses* folder.

21. Close the file.

Task 3

22. Re-open the file *Relax*.

23. Insert a paragraph break and clear line space after the words as you wash up! at the end of the first paragraph.

24. Create a table here that has 2 columns and 4 rows.

25. Enter the following data:

Programme	Benefits
1 month	Flexible
3 months	Weight loss and more energy
6 months	Gain extra year of life

26. Ensure that no border will be visible on any printout and all data is fully displayed.

27. Format the words Programme and Benefits to italic.

28. Right-align the heading Benefits and entries in that column only.

29. Save these changes to update the file.

30. Print one copy and then close *Relax*.

Task 4

31. Open the file *Music* from the *Courses* folder.

32. Save the file with the name *Guitars* into the *Daytime* folder.

33. After the words other European countries in the first paragraph, add the following sentence:

    During the 18th century the guitar attained its modern form, when the double courses were made single and a sixth string was added above the lower five.

34. Insert a paragraph break and clear line space after the words which was the highest in the first paragraph.

35. Delete the words in writing in the first sentence.

36. In the first paragraph, move the sentence beginning In its earliest form so that it becomes the *second* sentence after the words in Spain.

37. Apply bullets to the following list of guitarists:

    Eric Clapton
    Gary Moore
    Jimmy Page
    Slash

38. Apply double line spacing to the bulleted list only.

39. Indent the text Popular guitarists from the left margin.

40. Replace the word device with the word instrument wherever it occurs in the text (twice).

41. In the footer, add your name and the automatic filename.

42. Carry out a word count and add the figure at the bottom of the document.

43. Save the file and print one copy.

44. Close all files.

Answer 26a

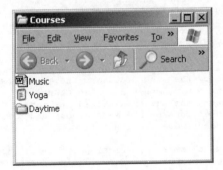

Answer 26b

Answer 26c

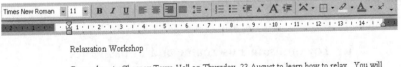

Relaxation Workshop

Come along to Chesney Town Hall on Thursday, 23 August to learn how to relax. You will be shown the top tips for staying stress-free in our busy modern world and will be provided with simple exercises you can perform at work, when watching TV or even as you wash up!

Programme	*Benefits*
1 month	Flexible
3 months	Weight loss and more energy
6 months	Gain extra year of life

Your teacher will be the television celebrity Keep Fit guru Madeleine Switchback.

The workshop starts at 6.00 p.m. and will finish at 9.00 p.m. Soft drinks are included.

```
The Guitar

A guitar-like instrument has existed since ancient times,
but the first mention of the guitar proper is found in
14th-century documents and it appears to have originated
in Spain.  In its earliest form it had three double
courses or pairs of strings plus a single string which
was the highest.  The guitar used to be played in taverns
but many composers wanted to promote it to concert level.

By the late 17th century a fifth course of strings had
been added below the other four and the guitar had spread
in popularity to many other European countries. During
the 18th century the guitar attained its modern form,
when the double courses were made single and a sixth
string was added above the lower five.

Perhaps the most famous classical guitarist in modern
times was Segovia, but in England Julian Bream was also
immensely popular.  However, in the 1930s, a new type of
instrument, the electric guitar, was developed for
popular music in the United States.

    Popular guitarists:
    •  Eric Clapton

    •  Gary Moore

    •  Jimmy Page

    •  Slash


181
```

Exercise 27

Task 1

1. Log on using a username and/or password.

2. Locate the folder *News* and rename it *Weather*.

3. Inside the *Weather* folder create a sub-folder and name it *International*.

4. Copy the text file *Maps* into the *International* folder.

5. Move the document *Europe* out of the *Travel* folder and into the *International* folder.

6. Delete the *Travel* folder and all its contents.

7. Take a screen print of the *Weather* folder showing its contents.

8. Take a screen print of the *International* folder showing its contents.

9. On the file showing the screen prints, add your name as a header and the automatic page number as a footer.

10. Print a copy of the screen prints and save the file(s) into the *Weather* folder.

Task 2

11. Create a new word processed document.

12. Set the page orientation to landscape.

13. Set the top and bottom margins to 4.5 cm.

14. Set the font to Courier.

15. Set the font size to 16.

16. Enter the following text, centre aligned.

    Health and Safety Notice

    Please note that the floors in reception have been waxed. Great care needs to be taken until further notice.

    From the 15th there will be major disturbance as several offices on the second floor are being refurbished. Some of the partition walls are being taken down as we move to open plan offices. Staff are asked to be patient during this time.

    In case of emergency, phone 0124 55367 for the Safety Officer.

17. Check for errors and carry out a spell check.

18. In the header, add the automatic file name and your name.

19. In the footer, add automatic page numbers and the automatic date.

20. Save the file as *Safety* into the *International* folder.

21. Close the file.

Task 3

22. Open the file *Safety*.

23. A table needs to be added to the end of the document. Insert a paragraph break and clear line space after the words **Safety Officer**.

24. Create a table of 2 columns and 5 rows.

25. Enter the following data:

Safety Officer	Hours
Judith Harwood	8.30 – 11.30
Peter Smale	11.30 – 2.30
Doreen Smith	2.30 – 5.30
Dan White	5.30 – 9.00

26. Format the text in the table to Courier font size 12.

27. Format the headings **Safety Officer** and **Hours** to bold.

28. Centre the heading **Hours**.

29. Right-align the times in the **Hours** column.

30. Make sure the table borders will be visible on any printout.

31. Save with the original filename and print a copy before closing.

Task 4

32. Open the file named *Tornadoes* provided in the *Weather* folder.

33. Rename it *Hurricanes* and save it into the *International* folder.

34. Insert the following text after the words **light winds above them** in the first paragraph: **When tornadoes move onto land, the heavy rain, strong winds and heavy waves can damage buildings, trees and cars.**

35. Move the final sentence in the second paragraph beginning **The term may come** so that it becomes the *first* sentence of that paragraph.

36. Delete the phrase **or the most violent or long lasting** in the third paragraph.

37. Apply numbers to the following lines of text:

    Southern Atlantic Ocean
    Caribbean Sea
    Gulf of Mexico
    Eastern Pacific Ocean

38. Replace the word **tornadoes** with the word **hurricanes** wherever it appears in the text (8 times).

39. Indent the final paragraph from the left margin.

40. Add your name and the automatic date in the footer.

41. Carry out a word count and enter the figure at the end of the whole document.

42. Save the file with the original filename and print a copy.

43. Close the file and any open files or folders.

Answer 27a

Answer 27b

Answer 27c

My Name

Health and Safety Notice

Please note that the floors in reception have been waxed. Great
care needs to be taken until further notice.

From the 15th there will be major disturbance as several offices on
the second floor are being refurbished. Some of the partition walls
are being taken down as we move to open plan offices. Staff are
asked to be patient during this time.

In case of emergency, phone 0124 55367 for the Safety Officer.

Safety Officer	Hours
Judith Harwood	8.30 - 11.30
Peter Smale	11.30 - 2.30
Doreen Smith	2.30 - 5.30
Dan White	5.30 - 9.00

Hurricanes

Hurricanes are severe tropical storms that form in one of
the following areas:
1. Southern Atlantic Ocean
2. Caribbean Sea
3. Gulf of Mexico
4. Eastern Pacific Ocean.

The term may come from the Indian words for evil spirits.
They need warm tropical oceans, moisture and light winds
above them. When hurricanes move onto land, the heavy
rain, strong winds and heavy waves can damage buildings,
trees and cars. The heavy waves are called a storm surge.
If the right conditions last long enough, hurricanes can
produce violent winds, incredible waves, torrential rains
and floods.

Hurricanes rotate in a counterclockwise direction around
an "eye" and have winds at least 74 miles per hour. There
are on average six Atlantic hurricanes each year and
although they are not the largest storm systems in our
atmosphere, they combine these qualities in a frightening
way.

Researchers continue to believe that there is a link
between hurricanes and El Nino, which is the
phenomenon whereby the ocean's surface temperature
becomes warmer than normal in the equatorial
Pacific. It appears that there are more tropical
storms and hurricanes during this annual event.

188

UNIT **2**

Creating spreadsheets and graphs

This unit will test your skills in creating and editing a spreadsheet, using formulae to perform calculations and printing copies of your work. You will also need to know how to produce and edit charts and graphs.

PART 1 SPREADSHEETS

EXERCISES 1, 2 AND 3

Test your ability to:

▶ Create a new spreadsheet

▶ Insert numbers and text

▶ Save and close a spreadsheet

Assessment Objectives: 1a and 5a

Exercise 1
1. Create a new spreadsheet.

2. In the first cell, enter the title: CAMP ROTA.

3. On the next row, enter the following 4 column headings: DAY, NAME, ACTIVITY and START TIME.

4. In the DAY column, type the following days of the week as row headings: Monday, Tuesday, Wednesday, Thursday and Friday.

5. Now add the data as set out below:

	A	B	C	D	E
1	CAMP ROTA				
2	DAY	NAME	ACTIVITY	START TIME	
3	Monday	Sally	Cooking	12	
4	Tuesday	Peter	Beds	10	
5	Wednesday	Marian	Lead walk	2	
6	Thursday	Doug	Cooking	12	
7	Friday	Steve	Wash-up	3	

6. Save as *Rota* and then close the file.

Exercise 2

1. Start a new spreadsheet and type the following title: SWEENEY SHARE PRICES.

2. On the next row, enter three column headings: DATE, PRICE and DEALER.

3. Type the following data, accepting any style of date that appears, e.g. 1/1/06 or 1 Jan 2006 etc:

	A	B	C	D
1	SWEENEY SHARE PRICES			
2	DATE	PRICE	DEALER	
3	01/01/2006	205	Todds Bank	
4	08/01/2006	217	Golden & Co	
5	15/01/2006	234	Tendingtons	
6	22/01/2006	219	Steward Share Dealers	
7	29/01/2006	198	Todds Bank	
8				

4. Save as *Shares* and then close the file.

Exercise 3

1. Start a new spreadsheet and type the title: MAGAZINES.

2. On a new line, add the column headings: NAME, COPIES and BILL.

3. Now enter the following data:

	A	B	C
1	MAGAZINES		
2	NAME	COPIES	BILL
3	STEVENS	3	3.5
4	ROE	5	6.45
5	STAMP	2	4.25
6	RUSH	6	15
7	HOOPER	2	4.75

4. Save as *Magazines* and close the file.

2

Test your ability to:

- Amend data

- Use formulae

- Recalculate data

- Widen columns to display data in full

Assessment Objectives: 1d, 2a, 2c and 5d

Exercise 4
1. Start a new spreadsheet and enter the title: PET SHOP.

2. Enter the following column headings on the next row: TYPE, VARIETY, COLOUR, IN STOCK, PRICE.

3. Enter the data as set out below:

	A	B	C	D	E
1	PET SHOP				
2	TYPE	VARIETY	COLOUR	IN STOCK	PRICE
3	Fish	Goldfish	Orange	20	0.8
4	Dog	Terrier	Black	2	10.5
5	Cat	Persian	Grey	4	25
6	Fish	Angel	Blue	12	1.5
7	Mouse	White	White	6	3.45
8	Rabbit	Long ear	Brown	2	6.75
9	Dog	Bulldog	Brown	1	32
10					

4. Save the file as *Pets*.

5. Now make the following changes, using any method, including find and replace:

   a) Angel should be changed to Fighting.

   b) There should be 5 Persian cats in stock.

   c) The price of a rabbit is 7.50.

   d) Terrier should be changed to Bull Terrier.

6. Widen any columns if necessary to display the data fully.

7. Now add a new column heading: VALUE.

8. Enter a formula to work out the *VALUE* of the stock of goldfish (*IN STOCK* multiplied by *PRICE*).

9. Enter formulae to work out the *VALUE* of all the other pets.

10. Save these changes to update the spreadsheet.

11. Close the file.

Answer

	A	B	C	D	E	F
1	PET SHOP					
2	TYPE	VARIETY	COLOUR	IN STOCK	PRICE	VALUE
3	Fish	Goldfish	Orange	20	0.8	16
4	Dog	Bull Terrier	Black	2	10.5	21
5	Cat	Persian	Grey	5	25	125
6	Fish	Fighting	Blue	12	1.5	18
7	Mouse	White	White	6	3.45	20.7
8	Rabbit	Long ear	Brown	2	7.5	15
9	Dog	Bulldog	Brown	1	32	32

Exercise 5

1. Start a new spreadsheet and enter the title PRINTSHOP.

2. On the next row, type the following column headings: ITEM, COST, ORDERS, INCOME.

3. Now enter the data shown below:

	A	B	C	D
1	PRINTSHOP			
2	ITEM	COST	ORDERS	INCOME
3	Poster A4	250	100	
4	Poster A3	365	56	
5	Business card	40	280	
6	Brochure	385	37	
7	Leaflet	400	255	
8	Newsletter	565	87	

4. The *INCOME* is calculated by multiplying the *COST* by the *ORDERS*. Enter a formula to calculate the *INCOME* for Poster A4.

5. Enter formulae to calculate the *INCOME* for all the other items.

6. Save the spreadsheet as *Printshop*.

7. Now make the following changes, widening any columns where necessary to display the data fully:

a) The orders for Business cards have increased to 375.

b) The Leaflet should be entered as 3-fold Leaflet.

c) The cost of the newsletter is 525.

8. Save these changes, ensuring entries in the INCOME column reflect the new figures.

9. Add a new row heading **Total** in the **ITEM** column. At the bottom of the **INCOME** column, enter a formula to total the entries.

10. Save these changes and then close the file.

Answer

	A	B	C	D
1	PRINTSHOP			
2	ITEM	COST	ORDERS	INCOME
3	Poster A4	250	100	25000
4	Poster A3	365	56	20440
5	Business card	40	375	15000
6	Brochure	385	37	14245
7	3-fold Leaflet	400	255	102000
8	Newsletter	525	87	45675
9	Total			222360

Exercise 6

1. Start a new spreadsheet and type the heading: **TIES**.

2. Enter the following data, leaving the **COST** column empty:

	A	B	C	D
1	TIES			
2	NAME	PRICE	BOUGHT	COST
3	Flowers	2.5	2	
4	Stripe	3.75	3	
5	Squares	3.75	4	
6	Spots	4.25	2	
7	Blue	1.99	6	

3. *COST* is calculated by multiplying *PRICE* by *BOUGHT*. Use a formula to work out the *COST* of **Flowers** ties.

4. Now work out the *COST* of all the other ties.

5. Save the file as *Ties*.

6. Now amend the **Blue** tie entry to read **Plain Dark Blue**. Widen the column to display the entry in full.

7. Save this change and then close the file.

Answer

	A	B	C	D
1	TIES			
2	NAME	PRICE	BOUGHT	COST
3	Flowers	2.5	2	5
4	Stripe	3.75	3	11.25
5	Squares	3.75	4	15
6	Spots	4.25	2	8.5
7	Plain Dark Blue	1.99	6	11.94

Test your ability to:

- Insert columns or rows
- Set page layout
- Copy (replicate) formulae
- Print spreadsheet data

Assessment Objectives: 1b, 2b, 5b and 5d

Exercise 7

1. Start a new spreadsheet and set the orientation to landscape.

2. Enter the title **EXAMS**.

3. Enter the following column headings: FIRST NAME, SURNAME, PHOTOGRAPHY, SILK SCREEN, POTTERY, DRAWING, AVERAGE.

4. Now enter the following data and ensure it is fully displayed:

	A	B	C	D	E	F	G
1	EXAMS						
2	FIRST NAME	SURNAME	PHOTOGRAPHY	SILK SCREEN	POTTERY	DRAWING	AVERAGE
3	John	Nash	24	33	18	27	
4	Harry	Lowry	37	35	16	29	
5	Wesley	Sanderson	20	29	22	25	
6	Rhona	Phillips	19	31	16	28	
7	Diane	Weston	36	30	21	27	
8							

5. Save the file as *Exams*.

6. Insert a new column headed **TOTAL** between **DRAWING** and **AVERAGE**.

7. Enter a formula to total John Nash's exam scores.

8. Replicate this formula down the **TOTAL** column to work out everyone's total score.

9. Insert a new row between Harry Lowry and Wesley Sanderson and add details for a new student: **Sue Blake**, 33 (photography), 28 (silk screen), 19 (pottery) and 25 (drawing).

10. Update the **TOTAL** column to take account of this data.

11. Make the following amendments:

    a) Rhona spells her surname **Philips**.

    b) Harry Lowry gained **19** marks in pottery.

12. The *AVERAGE* is calculated by dividing the *TOTAL* by the number of subjects (4). Enter a formula to calculate the *AVERAGE* marks for John Nash.

13. Replicate this formula down the **AVERAGE** column to calculate all the other students' average marks.

14. Save these changes and print a copy of the spreadsheet on 1 page.

15. Close the file.

Answer

	A	B	C	D	E	F	G	H
1	EXAMS							
2	FIRST NAME	SURNAME	PHOTOGRAPHY	SILK SCREEN	POTTERY	DRAWING	TOTAL	AVERAGE
3	John	Nash	24	33	18	27	102	25.5
4	Harry	Lowry	37	35	19	29	120	30
5	Sue	Blake	33	28	19	25	105	26.25
6	Wesley	Sanderson	20	29	22	25	96	24
7	Rhona	Philips	19	31	16	28	94	23.5
8	Diane	Weston	36	30	21	27	114	28.5

Exercise 8 1. Start a new spreadsheet with the title **MATERIAL**.

2. Set the left and right page margins to 2.5 cm.

3. Type the following column headings: **TYPE, COST PER METRE** and **AMOUNT**.

4. Enter the following data, ensuring it is all clearly displayed:

	A	B	C
1	MATERIAL		
2	TYPE	COST PER METRE	AMOUNT
3	Cotton	2.5	10
4	Velvet	4.85	8
5	Satin	4.5	3
6	Brocade	8	6.5
7	Lace	5.35	2

5. Save the file as *Material*.

6. Head a new column **TOTAL COST**.

7. The *TOTAL COST* is calculated by multiplying the *COST PER METRE* by the *AMOUNT*. Calculate the *TOTAL COST* for **Cotton** using this formula.

8. Replicate this formula to calculate the *TOTAL COST* for all the other materials.

9. Print a copy of the spreadsheet.

10. Add a new column after TOTAL COST headed TOTAL AFTER DISCOUNT. The discount is **5%** and the *TOTAL AFTER DISCOUNT* is calculated by using brackets as follows:

> *TOTAL COST* – (*TOTAL COST* multiplied by 5%)

Work out the *TOTAL AFTER DISCOUNT* for **Cotton** and then replicate this formula to work out *TOTAL AFTER DISCOUNT* for all other materials.

11. Insert a new row between Velvet and Satin for Ribbon. The COST PER METRE is 7.5 and the AMOUNT is 10 metres. Work out the *TOTAL COST* and *TOTAL AFTER DISCOUNT* for **Ribbon**.

12. Now add a new row heading Final Bill below Lace in the TYPE column.

13. Enter a formula to calculate the Final Bill for the materials by totalling the entries in the TOTAL AFTER DISCOUNT column.

14. Save these changes and print a copy of the amended spreadsheet to fit one page before closing the file.

Answer 8a

	A	B	C	D
1	MATERIAL			
2	TYPE	COST PER METRE	AMOUNT	TOTAL COST
3	Cotton	2.5	10	25
4	Velvet	4.85	8	38.8
5	Satin	4.5	3	13.5
6	Brocade	8	6.5	52
7	Lace	5.35	2	10.7

Answer 8b

	A	B	C	D	E
1	MATERIAL				
2	TYPE	COST PER METRE	AMOUNT	TOTAL COST	TOTAL AFTER DISCOUNT
3	Cotton	2.5	10	25	23.75
4	Velvet	4.85	8	38.8	36.86
5	Ribbon	7.5	10	75	71.25
6	Satin	4.5	3	13.5	12.825
7	Brocade	8	6.5	52	49.4
8	Lace	5.35	2	10.7	10.165
9	Final Bill				204.25

Exercise 9 1. Start a new spreadsheet and enter the title: HEIGHT.

2. On the next row, type the column headings: FEET, INCHES, CM (standing for centimetres) and METRES.

3. Enter the following data:

	A	B	C	D
1	HEIGHT			
2	FEET	INCHES	CM	METRES
3	5	0		
4	5	1		
5	5	2		
6	5	3		
7	5	4		
8	5	5		
9	5	6		
10	5	7		
11	5	8		
12	5	9		
13	5	10		
14	5	11		
15	6	0		
16	6	1		
17	6	2		
18	6	3		

4. Save the file as *Heights* and print a copy of the spreadsheet.

5. Insert a column between **INCHES** and **CM** headed **TOTAL INCHES**.

6. Widen the column to display the entry in full.

7. You calculate the **TOTAL INCHES** using brackets as follows:

    (*FEET* multiplied by 12) + *INCHES*.

    Enter a formula to work out the **TOTAL INCHES** for someone **5 FEET 0 INCHES**.

8. Replicate this formula down the column to work out all heights in **TOTAL INCHES**.

9. *CM* is calculated by multiplying *TOTAL INCHES* by 2.54. Work out the height in centimetres for someone **5 FEET 0 INCHES** and then replicate this formula to calculate all heights in CM.

10. Now use the formula *CM* divided by 100 to calculate the height in *METRES* of someone **5 FEET 0 INCHES**.

11. Replicate this formula down the column to calculate all heights in **METRES**.

12. Save these changes and print a copy of the final spreadsheet.

13. Close the file.

Answer

	A	B	C	D	E
1	HEIGHT				
2	FEET	INCHES	TOTAL INCHES	CM	METRES
3	5	0	60	152.4	1.524
4	5	1	61	154.94	1.5494
5	5	2	62	157.48	1.5748
6	5	3	63	160.02	1.6002
7	5	4	64	162.56	1.6256
8	5	5	65	165.1	1.651
9	5	6	66	167.64	1.6764
10	5	7	67	170.18	1.7018
11	5	8	68	172.72	1.7272
12	5	9	69	175.26	1.7526
13	5	10	70	177.8	1.778
14	5	11	71	180.34	1.8034
15	6	0	72	182.88	1.8288
16	6	1	73	185.42	1.8542
17	6	2	74	187.96	1.8796
18	6	3	75	190.5	1.905

EXERCISES 10, 11 AND 12

Test your ability to:

♦ Open a saved spreadsheet

♦ Delete columns or rows

♦ Align text

♦ Align numbers

Assessment Objectives: 1c and 4a

Exercise 10

1. Open the file *Pets*.

2. Right-align all column headings except TYPE.

3. Centre all entries in the IN STOCK column.

4. Delete the entire record for Persian Cats, leaving no empty cells.

5. Save these changes and print a copy of the spreadsheet.

6. Close the file.

Answer

	A	B	C	D	E	F
1	PET SHOP					
2	TYPE	VARIETY	COLOUR	IN STOCK	PRICE	VALUE
3	Fish	Goldfish	Orange	20	0.8	16
4	Dog	Bull Terrier	Black	2	10.5	21
5	Fish	Fighting	Blue	12	1.5	18
6	Mouse	White	White	6	3.45	20.7
7	Rabbit	Long ear	Brown	2	7.5	15
8	Dog	Bulldog	Brown	1	32	32
9						

Exercise 11   1.   Open the file *Exams*.

2.   Centre all the exam marks in the PHOTOGRAPHY, SILK SCREEN, POTTERY and DRAWING columns.

3.   Right-align all SURNAME entries.

4.   Delete the entire record for Harry Lowry, leaving no empty cells.

5.   Save these changes and print a copy before closing the file.

Answer

	A	B	C	D	E	F	G	H
1	EXAMS							
2	FIRST NAME	SURNAME	PHOTOGRAPHY	SILK SCREEN	POTTERY	DRAWING	TOTAL	AVERAGE
3	John	Nash	24	33	18	27	102	25.5
4	Sue	Blake	33	28	19	25	105	26.25
5	Wesley	Sanderson	20	29	22	25	96	24
6	Rhona	Philips	19	31	16	28	94	23.5
7	Diane	Weston	36	30	21	27	114	28.5
8								

Exercise 12   1.   Open the file *Heights*.

2.   Centre the data in the FEET, INCHES and TOTAL INCHES columns only.

3.   Right-align all column headings except FEET.

4.   Delete the rows displaying heights **5 FEET 0 INCHES** and **6 FEET 0 INCHES** only, leaving no empty cells.

5.   Save these changes and print a copy before closing the file.

Answer

	A	B	C	D	E
1	HEIGHT				
2	FEET	INCHES	TOTAL INCHES	CM	METRES
3	5	1	61	154.94	1.5494
4	5	2	62	157.48	1.5748
5	5	3	63	160.02	1.6002
6	5	4	64	162.56	1.6256
7	5	5	65	165.1	1.651
8	5	6	66	167.64	1.6764
9	5	7	67	170.18	1.7018
10	5	8	68	172.72	1.7272
11	5	9	69	175.26	1.7526
12	5	10	70	177.8	1.778
13	5	11	71	180.34	1.8034
14	6	1	73	185.42	1.8542
15	6	2	74	187.96	1.8796
16	6	3	75	190.5	1.905

EXERCISES 13, 14 AND 15

Test your ability to:

◆ Format numerical data

◆ Save a new version of a spreadsheet

Assessment Objectives: 4b and 5a

Exercise 13

1. Open the file *Printshop*.

2. Format entries in the **COST** column to show a £ sign and 2 decimal places.

3. Format entries in the **INCOME** column to show a £ sign (with or without separator) and 0 decimals (integer format).

4. Right-align all column headings except **ITEM**.

5. Save the amended spreadsheet with the name *Printshop 2*.

6. Print a copy of the spreadsheet and then close the file.

Answer

	A	B	C	D
1	PRINTSHOP			
2	ITEM	COST	ORDERS	INCOME
3	Poster A4	£250.00	100	£25,000
4	Poster A3	£365.00	56	£20,440
5	Business card	£40.00	375	£15,000
6	Brochure	£385.00	37	£14,245
7	3-fold Leaflet	£400.00	255	£102,000
8	Newsletter	£525.00	87	£45,675
9	Total			£222,360

Exercise 14   1.   Open the file *Rota*.

2.   Insert a new column between ACTIVITY and START TIME headed LENGTH IN HOURS. Right-align all column headings except DAY.

3.   Add the following data:

ACTIVITY	LENGTH IN HOURS
Cooking	1.5
Beds	0.45
Lead walk	2.5
Cooking	1.5
Wash-up	2.25

4.   Add a new column headed PAY PER HOUR, right aligned, and enter the following figures:

ACTIVITY	PAY PER HOUR
Cooking	4
Beds	3.5
Lead walk	6
Cooking	4
Wash-up	2.5

5.   Now add a final column, right aligned, headed INCOME.

6.   Enter a figure to calculate Sally's *INCOME* by multiplying *LENGTH IN HOURS* by *PAY PER HOUR*.

7.   Replicate this formula to calculate everyone's *INCOME*.

8.   Format entries in the INCOME column to show a £ sign and 2 decimal places.

9.   Format entries in the PAY PER HOUR column to currency but only 1 decimal place.

10. Format entries in LENGTH IN HOURS to show 2 decimal places.

11. Add a final row heading TOTAL PAYOUT and enter a formula to total entries in the INCOME column.

12. Format this entry to currency but 0 decimal places (integer format).

13. Save the file with the name *Payout*.

14. Change to landscape orientation and make sure you will print showing the gridlines.

15. Print one copy and then close the file.

Answer

	A	B	C	D	E	F	G
2	DAY	NAME	ACTIVITY	LENGTH IN HOURS	START TIME	PAY PER HOUR	INCOME
3	Monday	Sally	Cooking	1.50	12	£4.0	£6.00
4	Tuesday	Peter	Beds	0.45	10	£3.5	£1.58
5	Wednesday	Marian	Lead walk	2.50	2	£6.0	£15.00
6	Thursday	Doug	Cooking	1.50	12	£4.0	£6.00
7	Friday	Steve	Wash-up	2.25	3	£2.5	£5.63
8	TOTAL PAYOUT						£34

Exercise 15 **1.** Open the file *Heights*.

2. Format entries in the **METRES** column to number with 2 decimal places.

3. Format entries in the **CM** column to integer – no decimals.

4. Save the file as *Height formats*.

5. Print a copy and then close the file.

Answer

	A	B	C	D	E
1	HEIGHT				
2	FEET	INCHES	TOTAL INCHES	CM	METRES
3	5	1	61	155	1.55
4	5	2	62	157	1.57
5	5	3	63	160	1.60
6	5	4	64	163	1.63
7	5	5	65	165	1.65
8	5	6	66	168	1.68
9	5	7	67	170	1.70
10	5	8	68	173	1.73
11	5	9	69	175	1.75
12	5	10	70	178	1.78
13	5	11	71	180	1.80
14	6	1	73	185	1.85
15	6	2	74	188	1.88
16	6	3	75	191	1.91

Test your ability to:

◗ Add borders and shading

◗ Print a spreadsheet showing the formulae

◗ Print showing column and row headings

Assessment Objectives: 4c and 5e

2

Exercise 16 1. Create the following spreadsheet and save as *Drawing*.

	A	B	C	D	E
1	DRAWING MATERIALS				
2	ITEM	NUMBER SOLD	UNIT PRICE	DISCOUNT	TOTAL
3	ACRYLIC TUBE	9	3.75	5%	
4	WATERCOLOUR TUBE	23	2.99	5%	
5	WATERCOLOUR PAN	14	1.45	2%	
6	CALLIGRAPHY PEN	3	8.5	8%	
7	TRACING PAPER	11	5.75	10%	
8	COLOURED PENCIL PACK	18	7.5	5%	
9	BOXED OIL PAINTS	3	18.75	10%	
10	CHINESE PAINTING SET	6	24	10%	

2. Right-align all column headings except ITEM.

3. Format the UNIT PRICE column to currency with 2 decimal places.

4. Insert a new column between UNIT PRICE and DISCOUNT headed SALES INCOME. This is calculated by multiplying the *NUMBER SOLD* by the *UNIT PRICE*.

5. Enter a formula to calculate *SALES INCOME* for ACRYLIC TUBEs.

6. Replicate this formula to work out the *SALES INCOME* for all other items.

7. Format the entries to currency with 1 decimal place.

8. Enter your name a few lines below the spreadsheet.

9. Save these changes and print one copy of the spreadsheet, making sure all data is fully displayed.

10. Now make the following amendments:

a) TRACING PAPER costs £6.40.

b) BOXED OIL PAINTS should be changed to BOXED ACRYLIC PAINTS.

c) Only 19 WATERCOLOUR TUBE paints were sold.

11. Insert a new row below **TRACING PAPER** and add the following item: **SKETCH PENCIL PACK** sells at 5% discount, **13** were sold and the unit price is **£9.99**.

12. Enter a formula to calculate the *SALES INCOME* for this item and apply formatting in keeping with the rest of the spreadsheet.

13. *TOTAL* is calculated using brackets as follows:

    SALES INCOME – (*DISCOUNT* multiplied by the *SALES INCOME*).

    Enter a formula to calculate the *TOTAL* for **ACRYLIC TUBE** paint.

14. Replicate this formula down the column to calculate *TOTALs* for all other items and format the values to currency with 2 decimals.

15. Print a copy of the spreadsheet showing the formulae and column and row headings. (You can display all columns or only **ITEM** and those containing formulae.)

16. Now shade the cell containing the heading **DRAWING MATERIALS**.

17. Print a final version showing the values and then save and close the file.

Answer 16a

	A	B	C	D	E	F
1	DRAWING MATERIALS					
2	ITEM	NUMBER SOLD	UNIT PRICE	SALES INCOME	DISCOUNT	TOTAL
3	ACRYLIC TUBE	9	£3.75	£33.8	5%	
4	WATERCOLOUR TUBE	23	£2.99	£68.8	5%	
5	WATERCOLOUR PAN	14	£1.45	£20.3	2%	
6	CALLIGRAPHY PEN	3	£8.50	£25.5	8%	
7	TRACING PAPER	11	£5.75	£63.3	10%	
8	COLOURED PENCIL PACK	18	£7.50	£135.0	5%	
9	BOXED OIL PAINTS	3	£18.75	£56.3	10%	
10	CHINESE PAINTING SET	6	£24.00	£144.0	10%	
11						

Answer 16b

	A	D	F
1	DRAWING MATERIALS		
2	ITEM	SALES INCOME	TOTAL
3	ACRYLIC TUBE	=B3*C3	=D3-(D3*E3)
4	WATERCOLOUR TUBE	=B4*C4	=D4-(D4*E4)
5	WATERCOLOUR PAN	=B5*C5	=D5-(D5*E5)
6	CALLIGRAPHY PEN	=B6*C6	=D6-(D6*E6)
7	TRACING PAPER	=B7*C7	=D7-(D7*E7)
8	SKETCH PENCIL PACK	=B8*C8	=D8-(D8*E8)
9	COLOURED PENCIL PACK	=B9*C9	=D9-(D9*E9)
10	BOXED ACRYLIC PAINTS	=B10*C10	=D10-(D10*E10)
11	CHINESE PAINTING SET	=B11*C11	=D11-(D11*E11)
12			

Answer 16c

	A	B	C	D	E	F
1	DRAWING MATERIALS					
2	ITEM	NUMBER SOLD	UNIT PRICE	SALES INCOME	DISCOUNT	TOTAL
3	ACRYLIC TUBE	9	£3.75	£33.8	5%	£32.06
4	WATERCOLOUR TUBE	19	£2.99	£56.8	5%	£53.97
5	WATERCOLOUR PAN	14	£1.45	£20.3	2%	£19.89
6	CALLIGRAPHY PEN	3	£8.50	£25.5	8%	£23.59
7	TRACING PAPER	11	£6.40	£70.4	10%	£63.36
8	SKETCH PENCIL PACK	13	£9.99	£129.9	5%	£123.38
9	COLOURED PENCIL PACK	18	£7.50	£135.0	5%	£128.25
10	BOXED ACRYLIC PAINTS	3	£18.75	£56.3	10%	£50.63
11	CHINESE PAINTING SET	6	£24.00	£144.0	10%	£129.60
12						

2

Exercise 17 **1.** Create the following spreadsheet showing expenses in an office and save as *Expenses*.

	A	B	C	D	E	F
1	EXPENSES					
2	DATES	POSTAGE	REFRESHMENT	DISKS	CLEANING	TRAVEL
3	April	27.5	6.5	20	25	83.56
4	May	45.75	2.95	18.5	25	19.22
5	June	16	4.8	12	25	2.78
6	July	28.25	6	44	27	18.33
7	August	12.5	2.48	9	27	207.99
8	September	19.22	15.3	16	27	112.3

2. Format the entries as follows:

a) All column headings except DATES centre-align.

b) All figures to currency with 2 decimal places.

3. Add a new column after TRAVEL headed MONTHLY TOTAL. This is calcu-lated by adding together figures for POSTAGE, REFRESHMENT, DISKS, CLEANING and TRAVEL. Enter a formula to calculate the MONTHLY TOTAL for April.

4. Replicate the formula down the column to calculate all MONTHLY TOTALs.

5. Now head a new row TOTAL and enter a formula to calculate the TOTAL spent on POSTAGE.

6. Replicate this formula across the row to calculate the TOTAL for all other items.

7. Insert a new column between DISKS and CLEANING headed EQUIPMENT and enter £150.50 for June and £319.75 for August. Format the entries to currency and calculate a TOTAL at the bottom of the column.

8. Make sure the MONTHLY TOTAL column is updated to take account of the new entries.

9. Print a copy of the spreadsheet showing the values, not the formulae.

10. The office was closed for one month. Delete the entire entry for May, ensuring totals are updated.

11. Add a new row headed **AVERAGE** and enter a formula to calculate the *AVERAGE* expenditure on **POSTAGE** (*TOTAL* divided by 5).

12. Replicate this across the row to calculate *AVERAGEs* for all items.

13. Format the **AVERAGE** entries to currency with 0 decimals.

14. Save these changes and print the spreadsheet showing the formulae and column and row headings.

15. Now add a border round the cells containing the months and then print the spreadsheet showing the values.

16. Close the file.

Answer 17a

	A	B	C	D	E	F	G	H
1	EXPENSES							
2	DATES	POSTAGE	REFRESHMENT	DISKS	EQUIPMENT	CLEANING	TRAVEL	MONTHLY TOTAL
3	April	£27.50	£6.50	£20.00		£25.00	£83.56	£162.56
4	May	£45.75	£2.95	£18.50		£25.00	£19.22	£111.42
5	June	£16.00	£4.80	£12.00	£150.50	£25.00	£2.78	£211.08
6	July	£28.25	£6.00	£44.00		£27.00	£18.33	£123.58
7	August	£12.50	£2.48	£9.00	£319.75	£27.00	£207.99	£578.72
8	September	£19.22	£15.30	£16.00		£27.00	£112.30	£189.82
9	TOTAL	£149.22	£38.03	£119.50	£470.25	£156.00	£444.18	

Answer 17b

	A	B	C	D	E	F	G	H
1	EXPENSES							
2	DATES	POSTAGE	REFRESHMENT	DISKS	EQUIPMENT	CLEANING	TRAVEL	MONTHLY TOTAL
3	April	27.5	6.5	20		25	83.56	=SUM(B3:G3)
4	June	16	4.8	12	150.5	25	2.78	=SUM(B4:G4)
5	July	28.25	6	44		27	18.33	=SUM(B5:G5)
6	August	12.5	2.48	9	319.75	27	207.99	=SUM(B6:G6)
7	September	19.22	15.3	16		27	112.3	=SUM(B7:G7)
8	TOTAL	=SUM(B3:B7)	=SUM(C3:C7)	=SUM(D3:D7)	=SUM(E3:E7)	=SUM(F3:F7)	=SUM(G3:G7)	
9	AVERAGE	=B8/5	=C8/5	=D8/5	=E8/5	=F8/5	=G8/5	

Answer 17c

	A	B	C	D	E	F	G	H
1	EXPENSES							
2	DATES	POSTAGE	REFRESHMENT	DISKS	EQUIPMENT	CLEANING	TRAVEL	MONTHLY TOTAL
3	April	£27.50	£6.50	£20.00		£25.00	£83.56	£162.56
4	June	£16.00	£4.80	£12.00	£150.50	£25.00	£2.78	£211.08
5	July	£28.25	£6.00	£44.00		£27.00	£18.33	£123.58
6	August	£12.50	£2.48	£9.00	£319.75	£27.00	£207.99	£578.72
7	September	£19.22	£15.30	£16.00		£27.00	£112.30	£189.82
8	TOTAL	£103.47	£35.08	£101.00	£470.25	£131.00	£424.96	
9	AVERAGE	£21	£7	£20	£94	£26	£85	

EXERCISES 1, 2 AND 3

Test your ability to:

◗ Open an existing spreadsheet (data file)

◗ Select a single data set

◗ Create a pie chart

◗ Display data labels

◗ Save a chart and data file

Assessment Objectives: 3a, 3b, 4d and 5a

Exercise 1 1. Open the file *Puzzle* or create the following spreadsheet:

NAME	PUZZLE-SOLVING (HRS)
Mr Benton	2
Mrs Haywood	6.25
Miss Stopes	4
Mr Jones	3.5
Miss Welling	6

2. Create a pie chart to display the time each person took to solve the puzzle.

3. Add data labels so that each sector clearly shows the time taken (values).

4. Save the file using the file name *Time taken*.

Answer

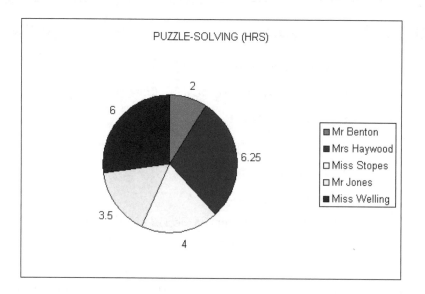

PUZZLE-SOLVING (HRS)

- Mr Benton
- Mrs Haywood
- Miss Stopes
- Mr Jones
- Miss Welling

Exercise 2   **1.** Open the data file *Holidays in France* or create your own using the following data:

MONTH BOOKED	NUMBERS
May	22
June	45
July	61
August	106
September	125
October	77
November	45

2. Create a pie chart to display the number of bookings that have been made over the period.

3. Display data labels to show the percentage bookings for each month.

4. Save the file as *Numbers*.

Answer

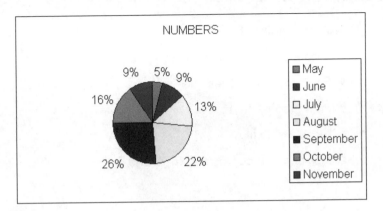

Exercise 3   1. Open the data file *Wine* or create your own using the following data:

REGION	PREFERENCE
Alsace	22%
Burgundy	25%
Loire	18%
Cote de Rhone	20%
Saumur	15%

2. Create a pie chart to display the wine preferences for each region.

3. Display data labels to show the name of each region and the percentage preference shown.

4. Save the file as *French Wine*.

Answer

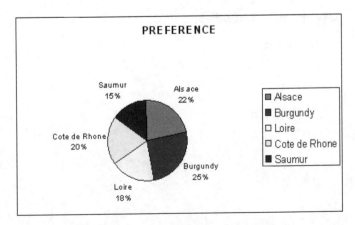

Test your ability to:

- Create a bar/column chart
- Enter graph and axes titles
- Print graphs/charts
- Close a data file

Assessment Objectives: 3a, 4d, 4f and 5f

Exercise 4 1. Open the data file *Groceries* or create your own using the following data:

FAMILY	WEEKLY GROCERY BILL
Dawkins	£45
Emmett	£68
Frenchman	£32
Walker	£70
Sweeney	£26

2. Create a column chart to show how much each family spends on groceries a week.

3. Enter the heading WEEKLY SPEND ON GROCERIES.

4. Give the X-axis the title FAMILIES and the Y-axis the title EXPENDITURE.

5. Ensure the names are visible on the X-axis.

6. Print a copy of the chart.

7. Save the file as *Spending*.

8. Close the file.

Answer

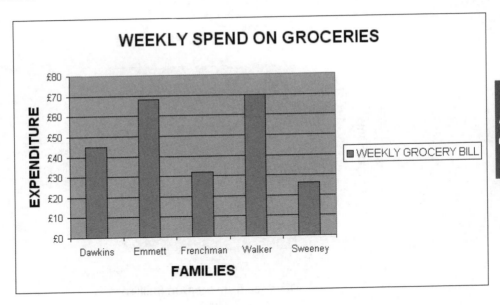

Exercise 5 1. Open the data file *Planets* or create your own using the following data:

Planet	Distance from the Sun (million km)
Earth	149.6
Jupiter	778.34
Mars	227.94
Mercury	57.91
Saturn	1427.01
Venus	108.21

2. Create a bar chart to show how far each planet is from the Sun.

3. Enter the heading THE PLANETS.

4. Give the X-axis the title Planet Name and the Y-axis the title Distance from the Sun (million km).

5. Print a copy of the chart.

6. Save the file as *Distances*.

7. Close the file.

Answer

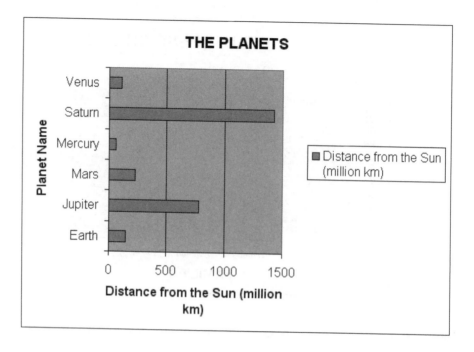

Exercise 6 **1.** Open the data file *Workshops* or create your own using the following data:

NAME	STUDENTS
Word processing	125
Spreadsheets	95
Desktop Publishing	145
Web pages	55
Writing CVs	167
Presentations	82

2. Create a column chart to show how many students are on each workshop.

3. Enter the heading WORKSHOP NUMBERS.

4. Give the X-axis the title WORKSHOP and the Y-axis the title STUDENT NUMBERS.

5. Print a copy of the chart.

6. Save the file as *Student Numbers*.

7. Close the file.

Answer

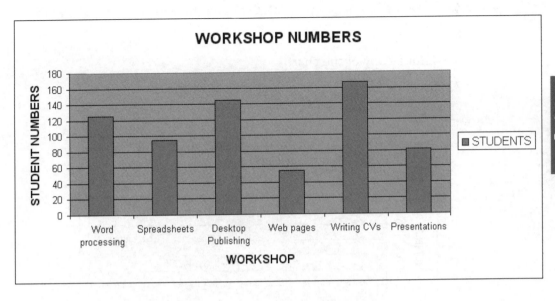

EXERCISES 7, 8 AND 9

Test your ability to:

◆ Select a subset of a single data set

◆ Use a legend where appropriate

Assessment Objectives: 3b and 4g

Exercise 7   1.   Open the data file *Survey* or create your own using the following data:

COLOUR	CARS IN JANUARY	CARS IN FEBRUARY	CARS IN MARCH
Red	5	7	3
Blue	20	18	8
Black	32	27	12
Silver	24	30	26
Yellow	1	0	2

2.   Create a column chart showing the number of cars surveyed during January *only*.

3. Give the chart the heading JANUARY CARS.

4. Give the X-axis the title COLOUR and the Y-axis the title NUMBER.

5. Remove the legend.

6. Print a copy of the chart.

7. Save the file as *Car Count* and then close the file.

Answer

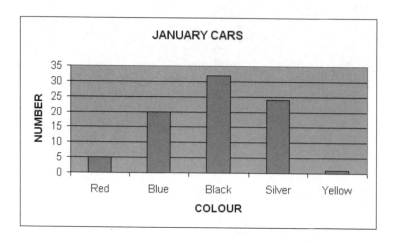

Exercise 8 1. Open the data file *Art Workshops* or create your own and enter the following data:

ART WORKSHOPS	CORFU PAINTERS	JILL BENTLEY ARTSCHOOL	ART FOR PLEASURE
Watercolour	£200	£125	£46
Pastels	£180	£110	£33
Drawing	£200	£130	£55
Oils	£250	£145	£75

2. Create a bar chart showing the cost of just the Watercolour workshops.

3. Give the chart the title WATERCOLOUR WORKSHOP COSTS.

4. Give the X-axis the title NAME OF SCHOOL and the Y-axis the title COST.

5. Remove the legend.

6. Save the file as *Cost of Art*.

7. Close the file.

Answer

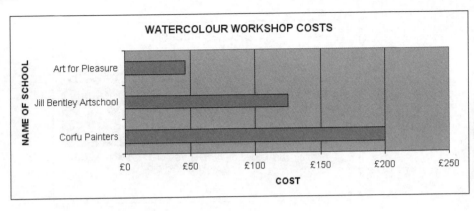

Exercise 9 1. Open the data file *Meat per Kilo* or create your own and enter the following data:

POULTRY	CHANDLERS	WELLINGTON STORES	MACDONALS
CHICKEN	£3.30	£3.95	£4.20
TURKEY	£6.60	£7.95	£5.50
GOOSE	£10.50	£12.45	£9.99
DUCK	£4.09	£4.65	£4.99
GUINEA FOWL	£11.35	£12.50	£10.85

2. Create a column chart showing the cost of chicken at all the stores.

3. Give the chart the title CHICKEN PRICES.

4. Give the X-axis the title STORE and the Y-axis the title PRICE.

5. Remove the legend.

6. Save the file as *Poultry Prices*.

7. Close the file.

Answer

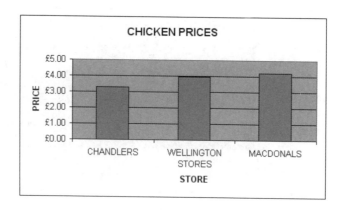

EXERCISES 10, 11 AND 12

Test your ability to:

◆ Create line graphs

◆ Select a comparative data set

Assessment Objectives: 3a and 3b

Exercise 10 1. Open the data file *Bonuses* or create your own and enter the following data:

NAME	JANUARY	FEBRUARY	MARCH	APRIL	MAY	JUNE
Marjory Clifford	£800	£880	£810	£900	£867	£902
Harvey Staples	£835	£897	£930	£1,024	£903	£945
Wallace Green	£790	£800	£875	£886	£778	£884
Doreen Stacey	£650	£650	£680	£740	£700	£698

2. Create a line graph to compare Marjory Clifford's income with that of Harvey Staples between January and April.

3. Give the graph the heading Comparative Income including bonuses Jan–April.

4. Give the X-axis the title **Months** and the Y-axis the title **Income**.

5. Ensure there is a legend.

6. Print a copy of the graph.

7. Save as *Comparative Income* and then close the file.

Answer

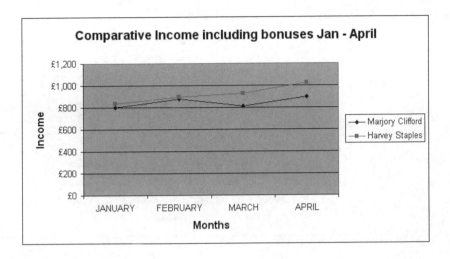

Exercise 11 1. Open the data file *Plant Growth* or create your own using the following data:

HEIGHT (CM)	GRASS	CRESS	BEANSPROUTS
Week 1	0.2	1.5	0.8
Week 2	0.9	1.7	1.4
Week 3	1.7	1.9	1.7
Week 4	2.4	2.2	1.8

2. Create a line graph to compare the growth of grass and cress seeds over the 4-week period.

3. Give the graph the title Comparing Grass and Cress.

4. Give the X-axis the title Weeks and the Y-axis the title Height in cm.

5. Ensure there is a legend.

6. Print a copy of the graph.

7. Save the file as *Comparing Growth* and then close the file.

Answer

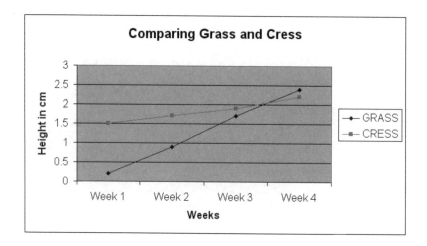

Exercise 12 1. Open the file *Savings* or create your own using the following data:

	January	February	March	April	May	June	July	August	September
Peter	£2.00	£3.50	£4.20	£3.95	£5.00	£5.50	£6.95	£8.50	£9.45
Daisy	£2.00	£4.00	£5.30	£4.32	£6.50	£9.45	£9.20	£10.35	£12.50
Mel	£2.00	£2.25	£2.85	£3.30	£3.60	£4.25	£6.40	£6.22	£7.50
Sandra	£2.00	£3.00	£4.00	£5.50	£6.75	£7.95	£10.30	£11.25	£13.25

2. Create a line graph to compare the savings of Peter and Daisy over the 9 months.

3. Give the graph the title **Peter and Daisy**.

4. Give the X-axis the title **Month** and the Y-axis the title **Amount Saved**.

5. Ensure there is a legend.

6. Print a copy of the graph.

7. Save the file as *Comparing Peter and Daisy* and then close the file.

Answer

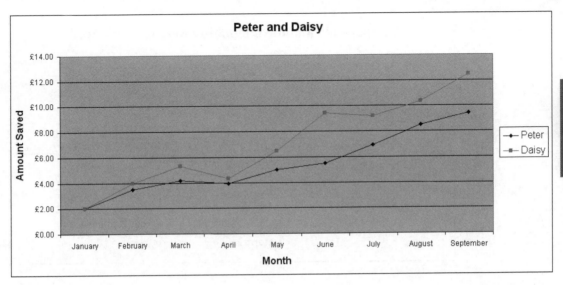

EXERCISES 13, 14 AND 15

Test your ability to:

‣ Set axes upper and lower limits

Assessment Objective: 4e

Exercise 13 1. Open the data file *Comparative Income* and the chart you created.

2. Set the Y-axis to display the range £600–£1,200.

3. Save the amended chart and print a copy.

4. Close the file.

Answer

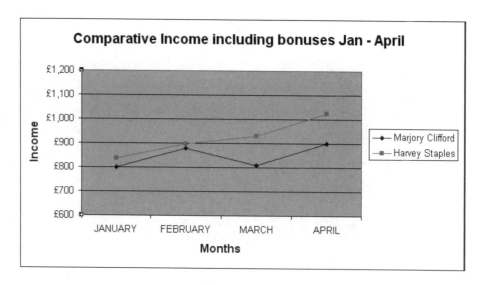

Exercise 14   **1.**   Open the data file *Fundraising* or create your own using the following data:

CLASS	FUNDRAISING 2003
Miss Keynon	£254
Mr. Wallace	£187
Mrs. Sibley	£257
Ms. Chatterjee	£310
Mr. Rohan	£165

  2.   Create a column chart to show the amount raised by all the classes.

  3.   Give the chart the title: MONEY RAISED IN 2003.

  4.   Give the X-axis the title: Class and the Y-axis the title: Amount.

  5.   Set the Y-axis to display the range £100–£350.

  6.   Remove the legend.

  7.   Save as *Money Raised* and print a copy before closing the file.

Answer

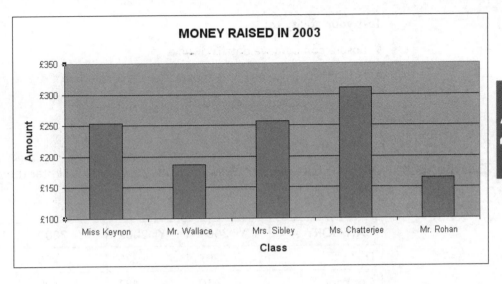

Exercise 15
1. Open the data file *Student Numbers* and the chart you created for exercise 6.

2. Set the Y-axis to display the range 50–170.

3. Remove the legend.

4. Save the amended chart and print a copy.

5. Close the file.

Answer

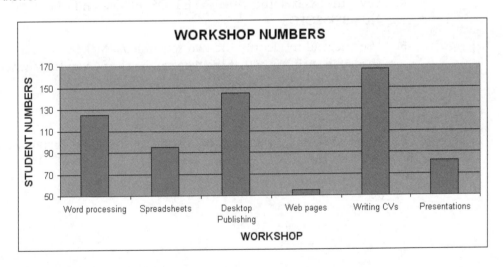

Test your ability to:

♦ Ensure comparative data is distinct

♦ Print charts or graphs on a separate sheet to the data

Assessment Objectives: 4h and 5f

Exercise 16 1. Open the data file *Book Sales* or create your own and enter the following data:

CATEGORY	Yr 2001	Yr 2002	Yr 2003	Yr 2004
IT	207	330	295	310
Cookery	410	487	489	506
DIY	330	328	299	345
Fashion	211	267	244	236
Photography	86	84	90	92

2. Create a comparative bar chart to show the sales of books in 2001 and 2002.

3. Give the chart the title BOOK SALES 2001 AND 2002.

4. Give the X-axis the title TYPES OF BOOK and the Y-axis the title NUMBER SOLD.

5. Use a legend to identify the two sets of bars. Make sure that the bars are shaded in such a way that the data can be clearly identified when printed.

6. Display values for each data series.

7. Save the chart and data.

8. Print one copy of the chart on a separate sheet and then close the file.

Answer

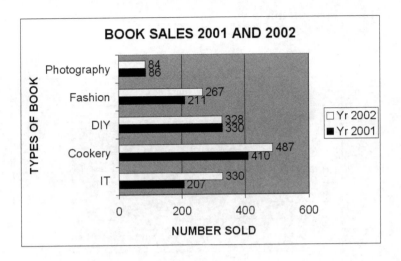

Exercise 17 1. Open the data file *Weight* or create your own using the following data:

Date	Lucy	Mavis	Amy
04-Jan	143	159	174
18-Jan	140	155	171
01-Feb	136	153	169
15-Feb	134	151	170
29-Feb	133	148	167
14-Mar	131	146	166

2. Create a comparative line graph to show the weight lost by Lucy and Mavis from 4 January to 14 March.

3. Give the graph the title Weight Loss.

4. Give the X-axis the title Date and the Y-axis the title Pounds.

5. Set the Y-axis range from 120–160.

6. Ensure that the lines (and data points if included) are distinctive and can be identified when printed.

7. Display the values for each data point on both lines.

8. Use a legend to identify each line.

9. Print a copy of the graph on its own sheet.

10. Save the graph and data file with the name *Pounds Lost*.

11. Close the file.

Answer

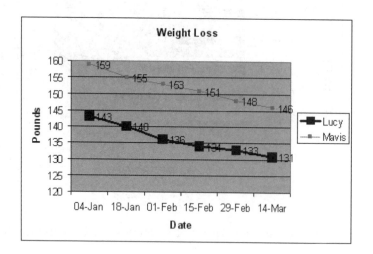

FULL ASSIGNMENTS – CREATING SPREADSHEETS AND GRAPHS

Exercise 18

Task 1

You are going to create a spreadsheet showing payments made towards the annual school trips.

1. Open a spreadsheet program and set the page to landscape orientation.

2. Set the page footer to show the automatic date and your name.

3. Enter the title SCHOOL TRIP.

4. On a row below the title, enter the 8 column headings as shown below:

Name	Destination	March	May	June	Total Payments	Full Cost(£)	Balance

5. Now enter the following information shown below:

Name	Destination	March	May	June	Total Payments	Full Cost (£)
Tom Wither	Belgium	50	45	75		250
Pete Winter	Belgium	50	60	50		250
Sally Townsend	France	30	35	45		180
Ron Harding	France	35	35	35		180
Susan Blake	Belgium	60	75	75		250
Mary Blake	Italy	55	50	80		275
Minnie Cleethorpe	Belgium	65	35	45		250
Dora Black	Italy	85	50	70		275

6. Save the file as *School Trip*.

7. Use a formula to calculate the **Total Payments** made by Tom Wither, by adding entries for March, May and June using the *SUM* function.

8. Replicate this formula down the **Total Payments** column to display the total payments made by all other pupils.

9. The **Balance** is calculated by subtracting the **Total Payments** from the **Full Cost** of the trip. Use a formula to enter the **Balance** for Tom Wither.

10. Replicate this formula to display the **Balance** for all the other pupils.

11. Print a copy of the spreadsheet in landscape orientation, making sure it fits on one page.

Task 2

12. Right-align all column headings except **Name**.

13. Display the entries in **March**, **May** and **June** as currency with 2 decimal places and **Full Cost** as integer (0 decimals) with no £ sign.

14. Format the **Total Payments** and **Balance** entries to currency with 0 decimal places.

15. Ron Harding is no longer going on the trip. Delete his record from the spreadsheet. Make sure you do not leave any blank cells.

16. There are two further amendments to make:

a) The payment made by **Susan Blake** in May should be increased to £85.

b) **Minnie Cleethorpe's** surname should be spelt **Claythorp**.

17. A new column is needed for payments made in **April**.

a) Insert the column between **March** and **May**.

b) Enter the heading **April**, right aligned.

c) Enter the figures for this column as set out below, and format entries to match the other payments:

Name	April
Tom Wither	£65.00
Pete Winter	£60.00
Sally Townsend	£25.00
Susan Blake	£25.00
Mary Blake	£90.00
Minnie Claythorp	£75.00
Dora Black	£55.00

18. Make sure that figures in the **Total Payments** and **Balance** columns reflect these changes.

19. Add a single outside border round all the column headings.

20. Insert a new row label **TOTALS** below the name Dora Black. Use the *SUM* function to total the entries in the **Total Payments** and **Full Cost** columns. Format these entries to currency and 0 decimals.

21. Save the spreadsheet with the original file name and print one copy on one page, in landscape orientation showing the figures.

Task 3

22. You are going to print a second version showing the formulae.

    a) Display the formulae.

    b) Make sure your printout will show gridlines and column and row headings (i.e. A, B, C etc. and 1, 2, 3 etc.).

    c) Check that it will fit on one page and be in landscape orientation.

    d) Print the entire spreadsheet showing the formulae in full.

    e) Save the file with the name *School2*.

23. Close the file.

Task 4

24. Open the data file *School Intake*.

25. Produce a line graph comparing the intake for Halbert School and St. Cuthberts for Years 2002–2005.

26. The years should be along the X-axis.

27. Give the graph the heading Halbert and St. Cuthberts Intake Comparison.

28. Give the X-axis the title Year.

29. Give the Y-axis the title Intake.

30. Use a legend to identify each line.

31. Make sure the lines (and any data points) are distinctive and can be identified when printed.

32. Display the values (numbers) for each data point on both lines.

33. Set the Y-axis range from 800–1550.

34. Save the file with the name *Comparison*.

35. Add your name and the automatic file name as a header.

36. Print a copy of the line graph on a separate sheet to the data.

37. Close the file.

2

Answer 18a

	A	B	C	D	E	F	G	H
1	SCHOOL TRIP							
2	Name	Destination	March	May	June	Total Payments	Full Cost(£)	Balance
3	Tom Wither	Belgium	£50.00	£45.00	£75.00	£170	250	£80
4	Pete Winter	Belgium	£50.00	£60.00	£50.00	£160	250	£90
5	Sally Townsend	France	£30.00	£35.00	£45.00	£110	180	£70
6	Ron Harding	France	£35.00	£35.00	£35.00	£105	180	£75
7	Susan Blake	Belgium	£60.00	£75.00	£75.00	£210	250	£40
8	Mary Blake	Italy	£55.00	£50.00	£80.00	£185	275	£90
9	Minnie Cleethorpe	Belgium	£65.00	£35.00	£45.00	£145	250	£105
10	Dora Black	Italy	£85.00	£50.00	£70.00	£205	275	£70

Answer 18b

	A	B	C	D	E	F	G	H	I
2	Name	Destination	March	April	May	June	Total Payments	Full Cost (£)	Balance
3	Tom Wither	Belgium	£50.00	£65.00	£45.00	£75.00	£235	250	£15
4	Pete Winter	Belgium	£50.00	£60.00	£60.00	£50.00	£220	250	£30
5	Sally Townsend	France	£30.00	£25.00	£35.00	£45.00	£135	180	£45
6	Susan Blake	Belgium	£60.00	£25.00	£85.00	£75.00	£245	250	£5
7	Mary Blake	Italy	£55.00	£90.00	£50.00	£80.00	£275	275	£0
8	Minnie Claythorp	Belgium	£65.00	£75.00	£35.00	£45.00	£220	250	£30
9	Dora Black	Italy	£85.00	£55.00	£50.00	£70.00	£260	275	£15
10	TOTALS						£1,590	£1,730	

Answer 18c

	A	G	H	I
2	Name	Total Payments	Full Cost (£)	Balance
3	Tom Wither	=SUM(C3:F3)	250	=H3-G3
4	Pete Winter	=SUM(C4:F4)	250	=H4-G4
5	Sally Townsend	=SUM(C5:F5)	180	=H5-G5
6	Susan Blake	=SUM(C6:F6)	250	=H6-G6
7	Mary Blake	=SUM(C7:F7)	275	=H7-G7
8	Minnie Claythorp	=SUM(C8:F8)	250	=H8-G8
9	Dora Black	=SUM(C9:F9)	275	=H9-G9
10	TOTALS	=SUM(G3:G9)	=SUM(H3:H9)	

Answer 18d

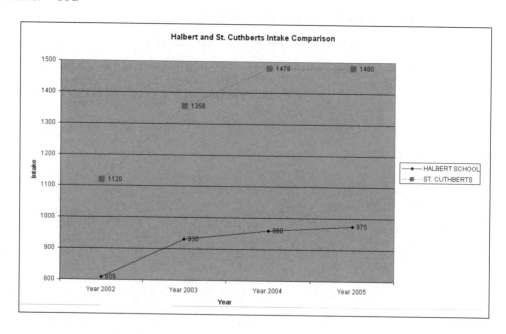

Exercise 19   A theatre company wants to use a spreadsheet to analyse the successes of plays put on around the country.

Task 1

1. Create a new spreadsheet.

2. Set the page layout to landscape orientation.

3. Enter the following data, leaving the TOTAL and INCOME columns blank:

	A	B	C	D	E	F	G
1	ENTERTAIN THEATRE COMPANY						
2	PLAYS	BATH	SWINDON	TRURO	TOTAL	TICKETS	INCOME
3	MACBETH	480	332	300		2.5	
4	CAROUSEL	795	850	756		3.75	
5	GREASE	1050	1254	1124		4.5	
6	WI NTER'S TALE	324	307	286		2.5	
7	CATS	996	1002	1005		4	
8	SCROOGE	875	978	950		3.5	

4. Enter your name and today's automatic date as a footer.

5. Save the file with the name *Theatre*.

6. *TOTALs* are calculated by adding bookings for BATH, SWINDON and TRURO.

   a) Insert a formula to calculate the *TOTAL* for MACBETH using the *SUM* function.

   b) Replicate this formula to show *TOTALs* for all the other plays.

7. You now need to calculate *INCOME* for each play.

   a) Insert a formula that works out *INCOME* for MACBETH by multiplying the *TOTAL* by the *TICKETS*.

   b) Replicate this formula down the column to calculate *INCOME* for all the plays.

8. Print one copy of the spreadsheet, showing the figures not the formulae, making sure all the data is displayed in full and that it is in landscape orientation and fits one page.

Task 2

9. Insert a new row heading OVERALL INCOME below SCROOGE. You can calculate the *OVERALL INCOME* by adding all the *INCOME* figures together. Insert the formula at the bottom of the INCOME column in the OVERALL INCOME row using the *SUM* function.

10. Right-align all column headings except PLAYS.

11. The figures for BATH, SWINDON, TRURO and TOTAL should be in integer format (zero decimal places).

12. The figures for TICKETS should be displayed with a £ sign and 2 decimal places.

13. The figures for INCOME should be displayed with a £ sign but in integer format (zero decimal places).

14. You now need to make the following amendments:

    a) Insert a new row between GREASE and WINTER'S TALE for the play MOUSETRAP. The bookings were as follows: BATH (1000), SWINDON (1245) and TRURO (967) and TICKETS cost £5.

    b) Bookings in TRURO for GREASE were 1178.

    c) CAROUSEL should be changed to CAMELOT.

    d) TICKETS for SCROOGE should be increased to £4.75.

    e) Make sure the TOTAL and INCOME figures are updated to include all these amendments and figures in each column are formatted correctly.

15. Add a single border round the names of the plays.

16. Save the file with the new name *Plays*.

Task 3

17. You want to find out the average bookings for each play. Insert a new column between TICKETS and INCOME headed AVERAGE and right-align the heading.

    a) *AVERAGE* is calculated by dividing the *TOTAL* for each play by the number of performances (3). Insert a formula to calculate average bookings for MACBETH. Replicate this formula down the column to work out average bookings for all the plays.

    b) Format the AVERAGE figures to display an integer format (zero decimals).

18. Save the spreadsheet with the same file name and print one copy showing the figures. Make sure all data is displayed in full and that the gridlines will show.

19. Now display the formulae.

20. Print a copy of the spreadsheet showing formulae in full and including row and column headings.

21. Save with the new file name *Play data*.

22. Close the spreadsheet.

Task 4

1. You are now going to create a chart comparing sales of music from the plays.

2. Open the data file *Music from the plays*.

3. Produce a column chart comparing the sale of music for Macbeth and Camelot from January–April.

4. The months should be along the X-axis.

5. Give the chart the heading Macbeth and Camelot Music Sales.

6. Give the X-axis the title Month.

7. Give the Y-axis the title Sales Figures.

8. Use a legend to identify each play.

9. Make sure the data for each play is distinctive and can be identified when printed.

10. Display data labels showing the values (numbers) on all the data points.

11. Set the Y-axis range from 100–450.

12. Save the file with the name *Music Comparison*.

13. Add your name and the automatic file name as a header.

14. Print a copy of the chart on a separate sheet to the data.

15. Update the file to save the changes and then close the file.

Answer 19a

	A	B	C	D	E	F	G
1	ENTERTAIN THEATRE COMPANY						
2	PLAYS	BATH	SWINDON	TRURO	TOTAL	TICKETS	INCOME
3	MACBETH	480	332	300	1112	2.5	2,780
4	CAROUSEL	795	850	756	2401	3.75	9,004
5	GREASE	1050	1254	1124	3428	4.5	15,426
6	WINTER'S TALE	324	307	286	917	2.5	2,293
7	CATS	996	1002	1005	3003	4	12,012
8	SCROOGE	875	978	950	2803	3.5	9,811

Answer 19b

ENTERTAIN THEATRE COMPANY							
PLAYS	BATH	SWINDON	TRURO	TOTAL	TICKETS	AVERAGE	INCOME
MACBETH	480	332	300	1112	£2.50	371	£2,780
CAMELOT	795	850	756	2401	£3.75	800	£9,004
GREASE	1050	1254	1178	3482	£4.50	1,161	£15,669
MOUSETRAP	1000	1245	976	3221	£5.00	1,074	£16,105
WINTER'S TALE	324	307	286	917	£2.50	306	£2,293
CATS	996	1002	1005	3003	£4.00	1,001	£12,012
SCROOGE	875	978	950	2803	£4.75	934	£13,314
OVERALL INCOME							£71,177

Answer 19c

	A	E	G	H
1	ENTERTAIN THEATRE COMPANY			
2	PLAYS	TOTAL	AVERAGE	INCOME
3	MACBETH	=SUM(B3:D3)	=E3/3	=E3*F3
4	CAMELOT	=SUM(B4:D4)	=E4/3	=E4*F4
5	GREASE	=SUM(B5:D5)	=E5/3	=E5*F5
6	MOUSETRAP	=SUM(B6:D6)	=E6/3	=E6*F6
7	WINTER'S TALE	=SUM(B7:D7)	=E7/3	=E7*F7
8	CATS	=SUM(B8:D8)	=E8/3	=E8*F8
9	SCROOGE	=SUM(B9:D9)	=E9/3	=E9*F9
10	OVERALL INCOME			=SUM(H3:H9)

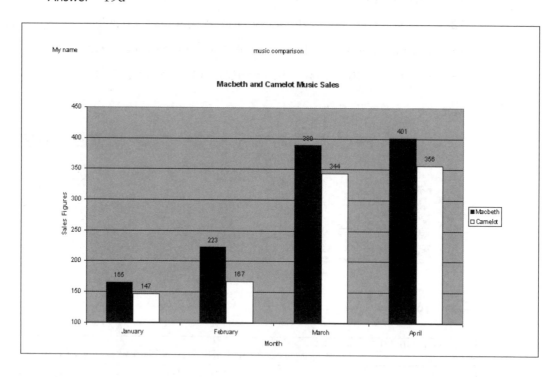

Exercise 20   A catering company wants to put details of its main dishes onto a spreadsheet.

Task 1

1. Open a spreadsheet application and enter the title SUPERFOODS.

2. Below this, enter the following headings: DISH, PORTIONS, CALORIES, SALES, COST, VEGETARIAN and COST PER PORTION.

3. Now enter the data set out below:

DISH	PORTIONS	CALORIES	SALES	COST	VEGETARIAN	COST PER PORTION
TRIFLE	6	440	22	6.5	YES	
PIZZA	8	650	14	9.5	YES	
CHICKEN MADRAS	6	945	59	8.25	NO	
FISH PIE	7	655	35	7.5	NO	
VEGETABLE LASAGNE	10	1025	21	10	YES	
KEDGEREE	9	920	15	7.5	NO	

4. Save the spreadsheet with the file name *Superfoods*.

5. Set the page orientation as landscape.

6. Add your name and the automatic date as a footer.

7. You want to work out the total sales for the month. Insert a new column between COST and VEGETARIAN labelled TOTAL.

8. Work out the *TOTAL* for TRIFLE by multiplying the *COST* by the *SALES*.

9. Replicate this figure down the column to find the *TOTAL* for all dishes.

10. Now add a new row label below KEDGEREE headed OVERALL INCOME. Use the *SUM* function to work out the total income by adding entries in the TOTAL column.

11. Now enter a formula that will work out the *COST PER PORTION* for TRIFLE by dividing the figure for *COST* by the *PORTIONS*.

12. Replicate this formula to show the *COST PER PORTION* for all the other dishes.

13. Save these changes, keeping the original filename.

14. Print a copy of the spreadsheet showing the figures, making sure all data is displayed and that it is in landscape orientation and fits one page.

Task 2

15. Format the TOTAL and COST PER PORTION figures to show the £ sign and 2 decimal places.

16. Format the COST figures as currency with 1 decimal place.

17. Right-align all column headings except DISH.

18. PIZZA is no longer provided. Delete the entry for this dish, leaving no blank cells.

19. Centre the title SUPERFOODS.

20. Border the cells displaying the COST PER PORTION figures only.

21. Save the file with the new name *Portions*.

Task 3

22. Now make the following changes to your spreadsheet:

a) CHICKEN MADRAS should be CHICKEN VINDALOO.

b) The COST of the FISH PIE should be £8.5.

c) TRIFLE provides 10 portions.

23. Ensure all figures reflect these changes.

24. Now add a new column between CALORIES and SALES to show CALORIES PER PORTION.

25. Work out *CALORIES PER PORTION* for TRIFLE by dividing *CALORIES* by *PORTIONS*.

26. Replicate this figure to work out *CALORIES PER PORTION* for all dishes.

27. Format the entries to show numbers in integer format (0 decimals).

28. Save the file with the same name.

29. Print one copy of the spreadsheet showing values, ensuring there will be no gridlines visible and it fits one page in landscape orientation.

30. Produce a second printout showing the formulae and row and column headings.

31. Save your spreadsheet with the file name *Calories*.

32. Close the file.

Task 4

The catering company wants to expand across Europe selling seasonal food.

33. Open the data file *Temperature* showing the average monthly temperatures in a variety of capitals.

DESTINATION	APRIL	MAY	JUNE	JULY	AUGUST	SEPTEMBER
AMSTERDAM	47	55	59	63	63	58
CORFU	60	70	90	95	95	85
DUBLIN	46	51	56	59	58	55
MINORCA	63	70	80	83	90	72
ROME	57	64	71	76	75	70

34. Produce a line graph comparing the temperatures in Amsterdam and Corfu between April and August.

35. Display the months along the X-axis.

36. Give the chart the title Compare Summer in Corfu and Amsterdam.

37. Give the X-axis the title Month.

38. Give the Y-axis the title Temperature.

39. Set the Y-axis to display the range 40–100.

40. Use a legend to identify the two lines.

41. Make sure that the data can be clearly identified when printed.

42. Display data labels showing the values (numbers) at each data point on both lines.

43. Add the automatic date and your name as a footer.

44. Print one copy of the graph on a separate sheet to the data.

45. Save the chart with the new file name *Corfu and Amsterdam*.

46. Close the file.

Answer 20a

	A	B	C	D	E	F	G	H
1	SUPERFOODS							
2	DISH	PORTIONS	CALORIES	SALES	COST	TOTAL	VEGETARIAN	COST PER PORTION
3	TRIFLE	6	440	22	6.5	143	YES	1.083333333
4	PIZZA	8	650	14	9.5	133	YES	1.1875
5	CHICKEN MADRAS	6	945	59	8.25	486.75	NO	1.375
6	FISH PIE	7	655	35	7.5	262.5	NO	1.071428571
7	VEGETABLE LASAGNE	10	1025	21	10	210	YES	1
8	KEDGEREE	9	920	15	7.5	112.5	NO	0.833333333
9	OVERALL INCOME					1347.8		

Answer 20b

SUPERFOODS								
DISH	PORTIONS	CALORIES	CALORIES PER PORTION	SALES	COST	TOTAL	VEGETARIAN	COST PER PORTION
TRIFLE	10	440	44	22	£6.5	£143.00	YES	£0.65
CHICKEN VINDALOO	6	945	158	59	£8.3	£486.75	NO	£1.38
FISH PIE	7	655	94	35	£8.5	£297.50	NO	£1.21
VEGETABLE LASAGNE	10	1025	103	21	£10.0	£210.00	YES	£1.00
KEDGEREE	9	920	102	15	£7.5	£112.50	NO	£0.83
OVERALL INCOME						£1,249.75		

Answer 20c – showing relevant formulae

A	D	G	I
SUPERFOODS			
DISH	CALORIES PER PORTION	TOTAL	COST PER PORTION
TRIFLE	=C3/B3	=E3*F3	=F3/B3
CHICKEN VINDALOO	=C4/B4	=E4*F4	=F4/B4
FISH PIE	=C5/B5	=E5*F5	=F5/B5
VEGETABLE LASAGNE	=C6/B6	=E6*F6	=F6/B6
KEDGEREE	=C7/B7	=E7*F7	=F7/B7
OVERALL INCOME		=SUM(G3:G7)	

Answer   20d

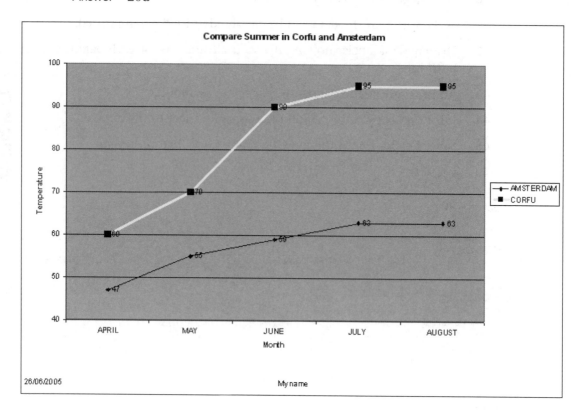

UNIT 3

Database manipulation

This unit tests your skills in entering and amending database records and searching for specific records meeting various criteria. You will also need to know how to sort records and limit the results of your search. New for the 2006 syllabus is the ability to create and amend reports.

Before starting the exercises, open the CD-ROM, select all the closed files and copy them across into a folder on your computer.

EXERCISES 1, 2 AND 3

Test your ability to:

- Open a database
- Open a table of data
- Enter records
- Close a database file

Assessment Objectives: 1a and 1b

Exercise 1   1.   Open the file *Holidays* and then the *Hotels* table, or create your own and enter the following records:

Hotels : Table

Name	Location	Rating	Food speciality	Seating	Open at Christmas	Average Meal Cost	Bedrooms
Golden Cross	Maidenhead	3	Fish	40	☑	£25.00	30
Epicure	Slough	2	French	25	☐	£45.00	40
Gabosh	London	4	Middle East	37	☑	£30.00	35
Tandoori Nights	Swindon	3	Indian	55	☑	£22.00	60
Grubbins	Maidenhead	3	Vegetarian	24	☐	£18.00	38
Swish	Slough	2	French	44	☑	£65.00	53
Foodie	London	4	Vegetarian	18	☐	£22.00	14
Salmondo	Swindon	3	Fish	52	☑	£85.00	60
Lettuce Inn	Slough	3	Vegetarian	30	☑	£20.00	36
Pandora	London	2	Indian	28	☑	£28.00	40
Tasty	Maidenhead	3	Vegetarian	25	☑	£19.00	29

2. Now add the following three records:

a) The Regency in Reading has a 4 rating and offers French food in the restaurant which seats 35 people. It opens at Christmas, has 40 bedrooms and the average meal costs £56.

b) The Cap Ferret in London has a French restaurant with 34 seats and meals average £90. The rating is 4, there are 60 bedrooms and it is not open at Christmas.

c) The Lamb in Slough offers fish as a speciality in the restaurant which seats 12 people. Meals average £35 and it is open at Christmas. The hotel has 16 bedrooms and has a 3 rating.

3. Save and close the file.

Answer

Hotels : Table

Name	Location	Rating	Food speciality	Seating	Open at Christmas	Average Meal Cost	Bedrooms
Golden Cross	Maidenhead	3	Fish	40	☑	£25.00	30
Epicure	Slough	2	French	25	☐	£45.00	40
Gabosh	London	4	Middle East	37	☑	£30.00	35
Tandoori Nights	Swindon	3	Indian	55	☑	£22.00	60
Grubbins	Maidenhead	3	Vegetarian	24	☐	£18.00	38
Swish	Slough	2	French	44	☑	£65.00	53
Foodie	London	4	Vegetarian	18	☐	£22.00	14
Salmondo	Swindon	3	Fish	52	☑	£85.00	60
Lettuce Inn	Slough	3	Vegetarian	30	☑	£20.00	36
Pandora	London	2	Indian	28	☑	£28.00	40
Tasty	Maidenhead	3	Vegetarian	25	☑	£19.00	29
Regency	Reading	4	French	35	☑	£56.00	40
Cap Ferret	London	4	French	34	☐	£90.00	60
Lamb	Slough	3	Fish	12	☑	£35.00	16

Exercise 2 1. Open the *Cars* database file and *Car Details* table, or create your own and enter the following records:

Car Details : Table

Make	Model	Doors	Colour	Miles	Price	Per month
Fiesta	1.8D	3	Red	14300	£4,995	£129
Mondeo	1.8TD	5	White	26000	£8,675	£144
Granada	2.0 GHIA AUTO	4	Blue	75000	£6,574	£125
Metro	1.4SL	5	Red	14356	£3,885	£200
Escort	1.4LX	5	Green	11000	£8,756	£199
Mondeo	1.8 Verona	5	Green	39886	£7,453	£149
Micra	1.4 16V Activ	5	Silver	59000	£4,955	£125
Corsa	1.2 SXJ	3	Black	31000	£4,500	£90
Vectra	140 SRj	4	Grey	127000	£2,500	£105

2. Now add the following records:

   a) Citroen AX 1.0 Spree has 3 doors, is blue and has 71,440 miles on the clock. It costs £1,799 or £150 a month.

   b) Peugeot 1.1 Zest has 3 doors, is red and has done 33,000 miles. It costs £3,995 or £120 per month.

   c) Golf 1.4 with 5 doors, is blue and has done 67,000 miles. It costs £1,250 or £90 per month.

3. Save and close the file.

Answer

Make	Model	Doors	Colour	Miles	Price	Per month
Fiesta	1.8D	3	Red	14300	£4,995	£129
Mondeo	1.8TD	5	White	26000	£8,675	£144
Granada	2.0 GHIA AUTO	4	Blue	75000	£6,574	£125
Metro	1.4SL	5	Red	14356	£3,885	£200
Escort	1.4LX	5	Green	11000	£8,756	£199
Mondeo	1.8 Verona	5	Green	39886	£7,453	£149
Micra	1.4 16V Activ	5	Silver	59000	£4,955	£125
Corsa	1.2 SXJ	3	Black	31000	£4,500	£90
Vectra	140 SRj	4	Grey	127000	£2,500	£105
Citroen	AX 1.0 Spree	3	Blue	71440	£1,799	£150
Peugeot	1.1 Zest	3	Red	33000	£3,995	£120
Golf	1.4	5	Blue	67000	£1,250	£90

Car Details : Table

Exercise 3 1. Open the file *Sports* and the table *Students* or create your own and enter the following records:

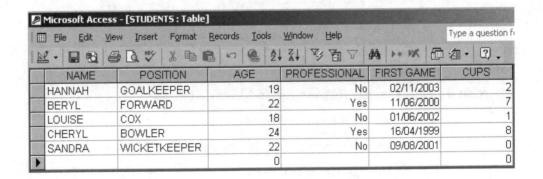

NAME	POSITION	AGE	PROFESSIONAL	FIRST GAME	CUPS
HANNAH	GOALKEEPER	19	No	02/11/2003	2
BERYL	FORWARD	22	Yes	11/06/2000	7
LOUISE	COX	18	No	01/06/2002	1
CHERYL	BOWLER	24	Yes	16/04/1999	8
SANDRA	WICKETKEEPER	22	No	09/08/2001	0
		0			0

2. Enter 3 more records:

   a) DAVINA has the position of STROKE, 25, NOT PROFESSIONAL, date of FIRST GAME 22/8/01, has 3 CUPS.

b) MARY swims BACKSTROKE, age 16, IS PROFESSIONAL, FIRST GAME 2/9/00, has 10 CUPS.

c) TRICIA is a FORWARD, 21, PROFESSIONAL, FIRST GAME 2/9/02, has 1 CUP.

3. Save and close the file.

Answer

	NAME	POSITION	AGE	PROFESSIONAL	FIRST GAME	CUPS
	HANNAH	GOALKEEPER	19	No	02/11/2003	2
	BERYL	FORWARD	22	Yes	11/06/2000	7
	LOUISE	COX	18	No	01/06/2002	1
	CHERYL	BOWLER	24	Yes	16/04/1999	8
	SANDRA	WICKETKEEPER	22	No	09/08/2001	0
	DAVINA	STROKE	25	No	22/08/2001	3
	MARY	BACKSTROKE	16	Yes	02/09/2000	10
𝄗	TRICIA	FORWARD	21	Yes	02/09/2002	1
*			0			0

STUDENTS : Table

EXERCISES 4, 5 AND 6

Test your ability to:

▶ Amend records

▶ Display all entries fully

▶ Delete records

▶ Save your records

Assessment Objectives: 1c, 1d, 1f and 1g

Exercise 4

1. Open the *Holidays* file and *Hotels* table.

2. Make the following changes:

    a) The Salmondo should be the Pesce.

    b) The Pandora was rated 4.

    c) The average meal at the Golden Cross is £67.

3. Delete the entire record for the Foodie hotel.

4. Add the following new hotel record and widen all columns to display the data fully:

The Mill on the Cliff hotel in Swindon has a vegetarian restaurant seating 44. The average meal costs £38, there are 7 bedrooms, it is not open at Christmas and has a rating of 2.

5. Save your amended table and then close the database file.

Answer

Name	Location	Rating	Food speciality	Seating	Open at Christmas	Average Meal Cost	Bedrooms
Golden Cross	Maidenhead	3	Fish	40	☑	£67.00	30
Epicure	Slough	2	French	25	☐	£45.00	40
Gabosh	London	4	Middle East	37	☑	£30.00	35
Tandoori Nights	Swindon	3	Indian	55	☑	£22.00	60
Grubbins	Maidenhead	3	Vegetarian	24	☐	£18.00	38
Swish	Slough	2	French	44	☑	£65.00	53
Pesce	Swindon	3	Fish	52	☑	£85.00	60
Lettuce Inn	Slough	3	Vegetarian	30	☑	£20.00	36
Pandora	London	4	Indian	28	☑	£28.00	40
Tasty	Maidenhead	3	Vegetarian	25	☑	£19.00	29
Regency	Reading	4	French	35	☑	£56.00	40
Cap Ferret	London	4	French	34	☐	£90.00	60
Lamb	Slough	3	Fish	12	☑	£35.00	16
The Mill on the Cliff	Swindon	2	Vegetarian	44	☐	£38.00	7

Exercise 5

1. Open the *Cars* database and *Car Details* table.

2. Make the following changes:

   a) The Metro is Silver.

   b) The Vectra costs £2,850.

   c) The Corsa has done 44,000 miles.

3. Delete the entire record for the Mondeo 1.8TD.

4. Now add a further record and widen columns to display all data fully:

   Volkswagen, Passat 1.9 Turbo Diesel, 4 door, blue, 12000 miles costs £1,350 or £120 per month.

5. Save the changes and close the file.

Answer

Car Details : Table

Make	Model	Doors	Colour	Miles	Price	Per month
Fiesta	1.8D	3	Red	14300	£4,995	£129
Granada	2.0 GHIA AUTO	4	Blue	75000	£6,574	£125
Metro	1.4SL	5	Silver	14356	£3,885	£200
Escort	1.4LX	5	Green	11000	£8,756	£199
Mondeo	1.8 Verona	5	Green	39886	£7,453	£149
Micra	1.4 16V Activ	5	Silver	59000	£4,955	£125
Corsa	1.2 SXJ	3	Black	44000	£4,500	£90
Vectra	140 SRj	4	Grey	127000	£2,850	£105
Citroen	AX 1.0 Spree	3	Blue	71440	£1,799	£150
Peugeot	1.1 Zest	3	Red	33000	£3,995	£120
Golf	1.4	5	Blue	67000	£1,250	£90
Volkswagen	Passat 1.9 Turbo Diesel	4	Blue	12000	£1,350	£120

Exercise 6

1. Open the *Sports* file and *Students* table.

2. Make the following amendments:

   a) BERYL is 26.

   b) MARY is not a professional.

   c) TRICIA should be PATRICIA.

   d) LOUISE has 2 cups.

3. Delete the entire record for CHERYL.

4. Now add a further record and widen columns to display the data fully:

NAME	POSITION	AGE	PROFESSIONAL	FIRST GAME	CUPS
ANN-MARIE	CENTRE FORWARD	18	No	18/06/2003	4

5. Save these changes and close the file.

Answer

STUDENTS : Table

NAME	POSITION	AGE	PROFESSIONAL	FIRST GAME	CUPS
HANNAH	GOALKEEPER	19	No	02/11/2003	2
BERYL	FORWARD	26	Yes	11/06/2000	7
LOUISE	COX	18	No	01/06/2002	2
SANDRA	WICKETKEEPER	22	No	09/08/2001	0
DAVINA	STROKE	25	No	22/08/2001	3
MARY	BACKSTROKE	16	No	02/09/2000	10
PATRICIA	FORWARD	21	Yes	02/09/2002	1
ANN-MARIE	CENTRE FORWARD	18	No	18/06/2003	4

EXERCISES 7, 8 AND 9

Test your ability to:

- Replace specified data
- Rename a table
- Set page orientation
- Print a table of data

Assessment Objectives: 1e, 1f, 1g and 3b

Exercise 7 1. Open the *Education* file and the *Classes* table or create a new file and enter the following records:

Subject	Day	Start	End	Tutor	Room	Daytime	Class size
French	Wednesday	17:30	19:30	Wallis	J4	☐	12
Yoga	Tuesday	10:00	11:30	Machin	C3	☑	14
Drawing	Tuesday	18:00	20:00	Halley	J6	☐	20
Silversmith	Monday	18:30	21:00	Borham	C8	☐	6
IT	Wednesday	11:30	13:00	Mellors	J4	☑	16
IT Advanced	Thursday	17:30	19:30	Mellors	C4	☐	24
Dance	Monday	19:00	21:00	Knight	H2	☐	16
Upholstery	Thursday	10:00	12:30	Peterson	J6	☑	12

Classes : Table

2. Add a further three classes:

   a) Archery on Thursday at 15:30 to 17:30 in H2 with Denton. This is not a daytime class and there are 16 students.

   b) Chinese on Monday from 12:00 to 14:00 in J4. This daytime class has 10 students and is tutored by Clayton.

   c) New CLAIT tutored by Mellors in J6 on Monday from 11:30 to 13:00. There are 12 students in this daytime class.

3. Delete the entire record for the Yoga class as this is no longer offered.

4. Print a copy of the table in landscape orientation, ensuring all data is fully displayed.

5. It is decided to display days as abbreviations. Replace the following days of the week as shown:

   Monday to be replaced with MON.
   Tuesday to be replaced with TUE.
   Wednesday to be replaced with WED.
   Thursday to be replaced with THU.

6. Rename the table *Classes 2*.

7. Save these changes and print a copy of the amended database before closing.

Answer 7a

Classes : Table

Subject	Day	Start	End	Tutor	Room	Daytime	Class size
French	Wednesday	17:30	19:30	Wallis	J4	☐	12
Drawing	Tuesday	18:00	20:00	Halley	J6	☐	20
Silversmith	Monday	18:30	21:00	Borham	C8	☐	6
IT	Wednesday	11:30	13:00	Mellors	J4	☑	16
IT Advanced	Thursday	17:30	19:30	Mellors	C4	☐	24
Dance	Monday	19:00	21:00	Knight	H2	☐	16
Upholstery	Thursday	10:00	12:30	Peterson	J6	☑	12
Archery	Thursday	15:30	17:30	Denton	H2	☐	16
Chinese	Monday	12:00	14:00	Clayton	J4	☑	10
New CLAIT	Monday	11:30	13:00	Mellors	J6	☑	12

Answer 7b

Classes 2 : Table

Subject	Day	Start	End	Tutor	Room	Daytime	Class size
French	WED	17:30	19:30	Wallis	J4	☐	12
Drawing	TUE	18:00	20:00	Halley	J6	☐	20
Silversmith	MON	18:30	21:00	Borham	C8	☐	6
IT	WED	11:30	13:00	Mellors	J4	☑	16
IT Advanced	THU	17:30	19:30	Mellors	C4	☐	24
Dance	MON	19:00	21:00	Knight	H2	☐	16
Upholstery	THU	10:00	12:30	Peterson	J6	☑	12
Archery	THU	15:30	17:30	Denton	H2	☐	16
Chinese	MON	12:00	14:00	Clayton	J4	☑	10
New CLAIT	MON	11:30	13:00	Mellors	J6	☑	12

Exercise 8 **1.** Open the *Animals* file and *Birds* table or create this and enter the following records:

Name	Type	Colour	Length (inches)	Habitat	Eggs
Herring	Gull	Grey	22	Coastal	3
Kestrel	Falcon	Grey	13.5	Moorlands	5
King Eider	Duck	Black	22	Freshwater pools	6
Golden	Eagle	Dark Brown	34	Barren mountains	2
Little	Owl	Grey Brown	8.5	Open country	4
Mistle	Thrush	Grey Brown	10.5	Woodlands	4
Reed	Warbler	Rich Brown	5	Reed bed	4
Sedge	Warbler	Warm Brown	5	Aquatic vegetation	6
Merlin	Falcon	Slate blue	10.5	Open moorland	5

2. Add the following two records:

    a) The Redwing is a Thrush that lives in forests, lays 4 eggs, is Sandy Brown and 8.5" in length.

    b) One type of Tree-creeper is the Short-toed which is 5" long, Brown, lays 6 eggs and lives in woodlands.

3. Delete the Reed Warbler record entirely from the table.

4. Print a copy of the amended table.

5. Now make the following amendments:

    a) Replace any entries for Grey Brown with Light Brown.

    b) Little Owl should be renamed Scops Owl.

    c) Replace all eggs entered as 6 with 7.

6. Save these changes.

7. Rename the table *Birds 2*.

8. Print a final copy of the table in landscape orientation before closing the file.

Answer 8a

Birds : Table

Name	Type	Colour	Length (inches)	Habitat	Eggs
Herring	Gull	Grey	22	Coastal	3
Kestrel	Falcon	Grey	13.5	Moorlands	5
King Eider	Duck	Black	22	Freshwater pools	6
Golden	Eagle	Dark Brown	34	Barren mountains	2
Little	Owl	Grey Brown	8.5	Open country	4
Mistle	Thrush	Grey Brown	10.5	Woodlands	4
Sedge	Warbler	Warm Brown	5	Aquatic vegetation	6
Merlin	Falcon	Slate blue	10.5	Open moorland	5
Redwing	Thrush	Sandy Brown	8.5	Forests	4
Short-toed	Tree-creeper	Brown	5	Woodlands	6

Answer 8b

Birds2 : Table

Name	Type	Colour	Length (inches)	Habitat	Eggs
Herring	Gull	Grey	22	Coastal	3
Kestrel	Falcon	Grey	13.5	Moorlands	5
King Eider	Duck	Black	22	Freshwater pools	7
Golden	Eagle	Dark Brown	34	Barren mountains	2
Scops	Owl	Light Brown	8.5	Open country	4
Mistle	Thrush	Light Brown	10.5	Woodlands	4
Sedge	Warbler	Warm Brown	5	Aquatic vegetation	7
Merlin	Falcon	Slate blue	10.5	Open moorland	5
Redwing	Thrush	Sandy Brown	8.5	Forests	4
Short-toed	Tree-creeper	Brown	5	Woodlands	7

Exercise 9   1.   Open the *Celebrities* file and *People* table or create your own and add the following records:

NAME	GENDER	FAMOUS FILM	VIEWINGS	COUNTRY
Michael Caine	Male	Alfie	4	UK
Mel Gibson	Male	Lethal Weapon	2	Australian
Julie Christie	Female	Far from the Madding Crowd	8	UK
Russell Crowe	Male	Gladiator	6	Australian
Meryl Streep	Female	Kramer v. Kramer	5	American
Dustin Hoffman	Male	Tootsie	10	American

People : Table

2.   Add three new records, widening the columns to display all the data:

NAME	GENDER	FAMOUS FILM	VIEWINGS	COUNTRY
Tom Cruise	Male	Top Gun	2	American
Faye Dunaway	Female	Chinatown	6	American
Jack Nicholson	Male	One Flew Over the Cuckoo's Nest	12	American

3.   Delete the entire record for Russell Crowe.

4.   You are going to replace the entries for GENDER with an abbreviation as follows:

a) Male should be M.

b) Female should be F.

5.   Amend the entry for Tom Cruise so that VIEWINGS show as 5.

6.   Save these changes and then close the file.

Answer

People : Table

NAME	GENDER	FAMOUS FILM	VIEWINGS	COUNTRY
Michael Caine	M	Alfie	4	UK
Mel Gibson	M	Lethal Weapon	2	Australian
Julie Christie	F	Far from the Madding Crowd	8	UK
Meryl Streep	F	Kramer v. Kramer	5	American
Dustin Hoffman	M	Tootsie	10	American
Tom Cruise	M	Top Gun	5	American
Faye Dunaway	F	Chinatown	6	American
Jack Nicholson	M	One Flew Over the Cuckoo's Nest	12	American

Test your ability to:

◆ Search for records on one criterion

◆ Save a query

Assessment Objectives: 1f and 2a

Exercise 10
1. Open the *Cars* file and *Car Details* table.

2. Create a query to find all cars with over 15,000 mileage.

3. Save the query as *Over 15000 miles* and print a copy displaying all the fields.

4. Now create a new query to find all cars that are £4,500 or under in price.

5. Save the query as *Price £4500 or under* and print a copy displaying all the fields.

6. Close the file.

Answer 10a

Over 15000 miles : Select Query

Make	Model	Doors	Colour	Miles	Price	Per month
Granada	2.0 GHIA AUTO	4	Blue	75,000	£6,574	£125
Mondeo	1.8 Verona	5	Green	39,886	£7,453	£149
Micra	1.4 16V Activ	5	Silver	59,000	£4,955	£125
Corsa	1.2 SXJ	3	Black	44,000	£4,500	£90
Vectra	140 SRj	4	Grey	127,000	£2,850	£105
Citroen	AX 1.0 Spree	3	Blue	71,440	£1,799	£150
Peugeot	1.1 Zest	3	Red	33,000	£3,995	£120
Golf	1.4	5	Blue	67,000	£1,250	£90

Answer 10b

Price £4500 or under : Select Query

Make	Model	Doors	Colour	Miles	Price	Per month
Metro	1.4SL	5	Silver	14,356	£3,885	£200
Corsa	1.2 SXJ	3	Black	44,000	£4,500	£90
Vectra	140 SRj	4	Grey	127,000	£2,850	£105
Citroen	AX 1.0 Spree	3	Blue	71,440	£1,799	£150
Peugeot	1.1 Zest	3	Red	33,000	£3,995	£120
Golf	1.4	5	Blue	67,000	£1,250	£90
Volkswagen	Passat 1.9 Turbo Diesel	4	Blue	12,000	£1,350	£120

Exercise 11
1. Open the *Education* file and *Classes 2* table.
2. Create a query to find all classes taking place during daytime.
3. Save as *Daytime Classes* and print a copy to display all the fields.
4. Now create a new query to find all classes that have 10 or more students.
5. Save as *10 or more students* and print a copy displaying all the fields.
6. Close the file.

Answer 11a

| Daytime Classes : Select Query | | | | | | | |
Subject	Day	Start	End	Tutor	Room	Daytime	Class size
IT	WED	11:30	13:00	Mellors	J4	☑	16
Upholstery	THU	10:00	12:30	Peterson	J6	☑	12
Chinese	MON	12:00	14:00	Clayton	J4	☑	10
New CLAIT	MON	11:30	13:00	Mellors	J6	☑	12

Answer 11b

| 10 or more students : Select Query | | | | | | | |
Subject	Day	Start	End	Tutor	Room	Daytime	Class size
French	WED	17:30	19:30	Wallis	J4	☐	12
Drawing	TUE	18:00	20:00	Halley	J6	☐	20
IT	WED	11:30	13:00	Mellors	J4	☑	16
IT Advanced	THU	17:30	19:30	Mellors	C4	☐	24
Dance	MON	19:00	21:00	Knight	H2	☐	16
Upholstery	THU	10:00	12:30	Peterson	J6	☑	12
Archery	THU	15:30	17:30	Denton	H2	☐	16
Chinese	MON	12:00	14:00	Clayton	J4	☑	10
New CLAIT	MON	11:30	13:00	Mellors	J6	☑	12

Exercise 12
1. Open the *Holidays* file and *Hotels* table.
2. Create a query to find all hotels that are located in towns beginning with S.
3. Save the query as *Swindon and Slough hotels* and print one copy displaying all the fields.
4. Now create a new query to find any hotel with a French restaurant.
5. Save as *French food* and print a copy displaying all fields.
6. Close the file.

Answer   12a

Name	Location	Rating	Food speciality	Seating	Open at Christmas	Average Meal Cost	Bedrooms
Swindon and Slough hotels : Select Query						
Epicure	Slough	2	French	25	☐	£45.00	40
Tandoori Nights	Swindon	3	Indian	55	☑	£22.00	60
Swish	Slough	2	French	44	☑	£65.00	53
Pesce	Swindon	3	Fish	52	☑	£85.00	60
Lettuce Inn	Slough	3	Vegetarian	30	☑	£20.00	36
Lamb	Slough	3	Fish	12	☑	£35.00	16
The Mill on the Cliff	Swindon	2	Vegetarian	44	☐	£38.00	7

Answer   12b

Name	Location	Rating	Food speciality	Seating	Open at Christmas	Average Meal Cost	Bedrooms
French food : Select Query						
Epicure	Slough	2	French	25	☐	£45.00	40
Swish	Slough	2	French	44	☑	£65.00	53
Regency	Reading	4	French	35	☑	£56.00	40
Cap Ferret	London	4	French	34	☐	£90.00	60

3

EXERCISES 13 AND 14

Test your ability to:

◆ Search on two criteria

◆ Sort records

Assessment Objectives: 2b and 2c

Exercise 13   1.   Open the *Employment* file and the *Jobs* table or create your own and add the following records:

COMPANY	JOB TITLE	SALARY	TOWN	VACANCY NUMBER	START DATE	CONTACT
SETTLES	CLERK	£16,000.00	LONDON	1	02/09/2005	JOHN REYNOLDS
SETTLES	MARKETING OFFICER	£35,000.00	LONDON	2	15/03/2005	MARY PIERCE
BALLARDS	HELPDESK	£19,000.00	LONDON	4	12/12/2004	WAYNE MANNING
SCOTS	SALES ASSISTANT	£15,500.00	BIRMINGHAM	3	14/08/2005	DON MISKIT
SCOTS	SALES MANAGER	£28,000.00	MANCHESTER	1	04/02/2005	DON MISKIT

▶

COMPANY	JOB TITLE	SALARY	TOWN	VACANCY NUMBER	START DATE	CONTACT
HAYWARDS	SALES ASSISTANT	£14,850.00	LONDON	2	17/02/2005	AMANDA DOBBS
WILFREDS	PURCHASING ASSISTANT	£23,000.00	LONDON	1	02/02/2005	STEWART HAVERS
GEORGE FASHIONS	SALES ASSISTANT	£19,900.00	LONDON	4	03/05/2005	HUSSEIN MASSAM
GEORGE FASHIONS	BUYER	£28,500.00	LEEDS	2	14/03/2005	HUSSEIN MASSAM
SPENDERS	TRAINEE PROGRAMMER	£20,000.00	LONDON	2	14/04/2005	STAN BERKLEY
SPENDERS	SYSTEMS ANALYST	£32,500.00	BRADFORD	3	12/02/2005	STAN BERKLEY
SPENDERS	IT SALES	£44,000.00	LONDON	2	08/04/2005	STAN BERKLEY
MILLETS	CLEANER	£12,500.00	WORTHING	1	19/12/2005	SARAH LEES

2. There are some errors in the records:

a) SPENDERS should be spelt SPLENDOURS. Replace the entry wherever it occurs (3 times).

b) There are 6 vacancies for HELPDESK staff.

c) The CONTACT at BALLARDS is WARREN MANNING.

3. It is easier if the towns are shown in code. Make the following changes:

d) LONDON to LDN

e) BRADFORD to BFD

f) BIRMINGHAM to BRM

g) MANCHESTER to MCH

h) WORTHING to WTH

i) LEEDS to LDS.

4. Print a copy of the amended table.

5. Design a query to display only jobs under £20,000 in London.

6. Sort the records in descending order of SALARY.

7. Save the query and print a copy of the records.

Answer   13a

COMPANY	JOB TITLE	SALARY	TOWN	VACANCY NUMBER	START DATE	CONTACT
SETTLES	CLERK	£16,000.00	LDN	1	02/09/2005	JOHN REYNOLDS
SETTLES	MARKETING OFFICER	£35,000.00	LDN	2	15/03/2005	MARY PIERCE
BALLARDS	HELPDESK	£19,000.00	LDN	6	12/12/2004	WARREN MANNING
SCOTS	SALES ASSISTANT	£15,500.00	BRM	3	14/08/2005	DON MISKIT
SCOTS	SALES MANAGER	£28,000.00	MCH	1	04/02/2005	DON MISKIT
HAYWARDS	SALES ASSISTANT	£14,850.00	LDN	2	17/02/2005	AMANDA DOBBS
WILFREDS	PURCHASING ASSISTANT	£23,000.00	LDN	1	02/02/2005	STEWART HAVERS
GEORGE FASHIONS	SALES ASSISTANT	£19,900.00	LDN	4	03/05/2005	HUSSEIN MASSAM
GEORGE FASHIONS	BUYER	£28,500.00	LDS	2	14/03/2005	HUSSEIN MASSAM
SPLENDOURS	TRAINEE PROGRAMMER	£20,000.00	LDN	2	14/04/2005	STAN BERKLEY
SPLENDOURS	SYSTEMS ANALYST	£32,500.00	BFD	3	12/02/2005	STAN BERKLEY
SPLENDOURS	IT SALES	£44,000.00	LDN	2	08/04/2005	STAN BERKLEY
MILLETS	CLEANER	£12,500.00	WTH	1	19/12/2005	SARAH LEES

Answer   13b

COMPANY	JOB TITLE	SALARY	TOWN	VACANCY NUMBER	START DATE	CONTACT
GEORGE FASHIONS	SALES ASSISTANT	£19,900.00	LDN	4	03/05/2005	HUSSEIN MASSAM
BALLARDS	HELPDESK	£19,000.00	LDN	6	12/12/2004	WARREN MANNING
SETTLES	CLERK	£16,000.00	LDN	1	02/09/2005	JOHN REYNOLDS
HAYWARDS	SALES ASSISTANT	£14,850.00	LDN	2	17/02/2005	AMANDA DOBBS

Exercise 14 1. Design a new query to find any jobs with a **START DATE** between February and May 2005 with **3** or fewer **VACANCY NUMBERs**.

2. Sort the records in ascending order of **START DATE**.

3. Save the query and print a copy of the records.

4. Now create a new query to find any jobs with a salary over £25,000 outside London.

5. Sort the records in alphabetical order of **COMPANY**.

6. Save the query and print the records.

7. Close the file.

Answer   14a

COMPANY	JOB TITLE	SALARY	TOWN	VACANCY NUMBER	START DATE	CONTACT
WILFREDS	PURCHASING ASSISTANT	£23,000.00	LDN	1	02/02/2005	STEWART HAVERS
SCOTS	SALES MANAGER	£28,000.00	MCH	1	04/02/2005	DON MISKIT
SPLENDOURS	SYSTEMS ANALYST	£32,500.00	BFD	3	12/02/2005	STAN BERKLEY
HAYWARDS	SALES ASSISTANT	£14,850.00	LDN	2	17/02/2005	AMANDA DOBBS
GEORGE FASHIONS	BUYER	£28,500.00	LDS	2	14/03/2005	HUSSEIN MASSAM
SETTLES	MARKETING OFFICER	£35,000.00	LDN	2	15/03/2005	MARY PIERCE
SPLENDOURS	IT SALES	£44,000.00	LDN	2	08/04/2005	STAN BERKLEY
SPLENDOURS	TRAINEE PROGRAMMER	£20,000.00	LDN	2	14/04/2005	STAN BERKLEY

Answer   14b

COMPANY	JOB TITLE	SALARY	TOWN	VACANCY NUMBER	START DATE	CONTACT
GEORGE FASHIONS	BUYER	£28,500.00	LDS	2	14/03/2005	HUSSEIN MASSAM
SCOTS	SALES MANAGER	£28,000.00	MCH	1	04/02/2005	DON MISKIT
SPLENDOURS	SYSTEMS ANALYST	£32,500.00	BFD	3	12/02/2005	STAN BERKLEY

Test your ability to:

◗ Present only selected fields

Assessment Objective: 2d

Exercise 15 1. Open the *Animals* file and *Birds* table.

2. Use a query to find any birds that are between 10"–20" in length and lay more than 3 eggs.

3. Display only the Name, Type, Habitat and Eggs.

4. Sort the records in descending order of Eggs.

5. Save as *4 or more eggs* and print a copy of the records.

6. Close the file.

Answer

4 or more eggs : Select Query			
Name	Type	Habitat	Eggs
Merlin	Falcon	Open moorland	5
Kestrel	Falcon	Moorlands	5
Mistle	Thrush	Woodlands	4

Exercise 16 1. Open the *Education* file and *Classes 2* table.

2. Create a query to find which classes run on Mondays earlier than 7 pm.

3. Display only the Subject, Class size and Room.

4. Sort the records in alphabetical order of Subject.

5. Save as *Monday Classes* and print a copy of the records.

6. Close the file.

Answer

Monday Classes : Select Query		
Subject	Class size	Room
Chinese	10	J4
New CLAIT	12	J6
Silversmith	6	C8

Exercise 17

1. Open the *Holidays* file and *Hotels* table.

2. Create a query to find out which hotels offering **Vegetarian** food can seat 25 or more people.

3. Display **Name**, **Location** and **Average Meal Cost** only.

4. Sort in descending order of **Average Meal Cost**.

5. Save as *Large vegetarian* and print a copy of the records.

6. Close the file.

7. Open the file *Entertainment* and the *Cinema* table, or create your own and enter the following records:

Film	Star	Date showing	Child Tickets	Adult Tickets	Special matinee
Ace Detective	Jim Carrey	02/07/2005	£4.50	£7.00	☑
Gladiator	Russell Crowe	24/06/2005	£5.50	£7.50	☐
Hook	Dustin Hoffman	14/09/2005	£3.50	£6.00	☑
Notting Hill	Hugh Grant	28/09/2005	£4.25	£7.45	☐
Odd Couple	Jack Lemmon	23/07/2005	£4.50	£7.00	☑
Rain Man	Tom Cruise	22/08/2005	£5.25	£7.75	☐
Wizard of Oz	Judy Garland	12/08/2005	£3.50	£6.00	☑

Cinema : Table

8. Create a query to find all films with the **Date showing** before September that have a **Special** matinee.

9. Display only the **Film**, **Star** and **Date showing**.

10. Sort the records in order of **Date showing**.

11. Save the query as *Matinee before September* and print a copy of the records.

12. Close the file.

Answer 17a

Large vegetarian : Select Query

Name	Location	Average Meal Cost
The Mill on the Cliff	Swindon	£38.00
Lettuce Inn	Slough	£20.00
Tasty	Maidenhead	£19.00

Answer 17b

Matinee before September : Select Query

Film	Star	Date showing
Ace Detective	Jim Carrey	02/07/2005
Odd Couple	Jack Lemmon	23/07/2005
Wizard of Oz	Judy Garland	12/08/2005

Test your ability to:

- Produce simple database reports

- Display data in full

- Add page headers and footers

Assessment Objectives: 3a, 3c and 3d

Exercise 18
1. Using the query *10 or more students* created in exercise 11, create a tabular report.

2. Title the report *Students Today*.

3. Save the report with the name *Student Report*.

4. Ensure all data is fully displayed.

5. Ensure the automatic date and page number are displayed in the footer.

6. Print a copy of the report on one page in landscape orientation.

7. Close the database.

Answer

Students Today

Subject	Day	Start	End	Tutor	Room	Daytime	Class size
French	WED	17:30	19:30	Wallis	J4	☐	12
Drawing	TUE	18:00	20:00	Halley	J6	☐	20
IT	WED	11:30	13:00	Mellors	J4	☑	16
IT Advanced	THU	17:30	19:30	Mellors	C4	☐	24
Dance	MON	19:00	21:00	Knight	H2	☐	16
Upholstery	THU	10:00	12:30	Peterson	J6	☑	12
Archery	THU	15:30	17:30	Denton	H2	☐	16
Chinese	MON	12:00	14:00	Clayton	J4	☑	10
New CLAIT	MON	11:30	13:00	Mellors	J6	☑	12

Exercise 19
1. Using the query *4 or more eggs* created in exercise 15, produce a tabular report in portrait orientation.

2. Give the report the title: *Egg laying Birds*.

3. Ensure all data is fully displayed.

4. Print a copy in portrait orientation on a single page.

5. Make sure the date is displayed in the footer.

6. Save the report as *Egg Layers*.

7. Close the file.

Answer

Egg laying Birds			
Name	*Type*	*Habitat*	*Eggs*
Merlin	Falcon	Open moorland	5
Kestrel	Falcon	Moorlands	5
Mistle	Thrush	Woodlands	4

FULL ASSIGNMENTS – DATABASE MANIPULATION

Exercise 20

Task 1

1. Open the database *Beds* and the *Bed Details* table.

2. Set the page to landscape orientation.

3. Print a copy showing all the records and field names in full.

4. Close the table.

5. Rename it *Bed Orders*.

6. Using codes for the SIZE field would be more efficient. Replace the existing entries as follows:

   a) KING becomes KG.

   b) DOUBLE becomes DB.

   c) SINGLE becomes SN.

7. The PRINCESS bed order has been cancelled. Delete this record from the table.

8. Three new orders have been placed. Add these to the database:

   a) CHARLETON has ordered a SLEEPWELL bed in BEIGE. It is a SN and costs £99. Delivery is on 5/10/2005.

   b) MANN has ordered a SN bed in WHITE costing £103. Delivery is on 18/9/2005 and the make of bed is SOFTNESS.

   c) The PRINCE bed, a DB in YELLOW, has been ordered by BILLINGS for delivery on 25/10/2005. The cost is £356.

9. Some of the data in the table needs to be amended.

   a) The PRINCE bed costs £392.

   b) The SLEEPY bed is PINK.

   c) The ASLEEP has been ordered by STONE.

10. Print all the data in table format, making sure all the records are fully displayed.

Task 2

11. The shop owner would like to know how many orders for king size beds have been taken that will be delivered over the next few weeks. Set up the following query:

    a) Select all KING SIZE beds with a DELIVERY date before 12/9/2005.

    b) Display only MAKE, CUSTOMER and PRICE.

    c) Sort the data in alphabetical order of CUSTOMER.

    d) Save the query as *Early Kingsize* and print the results in table format.

12. You now need to see how the more expensive, pale beds are doing. Set up the following query:

    a) Select all beds with a PRICE of more than £110 that are not GREEN in COLOUR.

    b) Display only the MAKE, SIZE and DELIVERY fields.

    c) Sort the data in descending order of DELIVERY.

    d) Save the query as *Over £110 not green* and print the results in table format.

Task 3

13. Now you need to find out who has ordered a double bed for delivery in October. Set up the following query:

    a) Select all DOUBLE SIZE beds where DELIVERY is after 30/9/2005.

    b) Display only the CUSTOMER, MAKE and PRICE fields.

    c) Sort in alphabetical order of MAKE.

    d) Save the query with the name *Double in October* and print the results in table format.

Task 4

14. Using the *Over £110 not green* query, create a tabular report in landscape orientation.

15. Title the report: *Beds Over £110*.

16. Save the report as *Over £110 Beds*.

17. Print a copy in landscape orientation to fit on one page.

18. Exit the software with all the data saved.

Answer 20a

BED DETAILS : Table

MAKE	CUSTOMER	SIZE	PRICE	COLOUR	DELIVERY
SLEEPY	BROWN	KING	£445	GREEN	02/09/2005
SNOOZY	HATCHETT	DOUBLE	£370	WHITE	23/08/2005
NIGHT-TIME	DROVER	SINGLE	£105	GREEN	15/09/2005
LULLABY	SMALL	SINGLE	£85	WHITE	10/09/2005
REST-EASY	TIVOTT	KING	£395	BEIGE	15/09/2005
ASLEEP	STEPP	DOUBLE	£404	YELLOW	08/10/2005
CALM	WAKEFIELD	KING	£575	WHITE	07/09/2005
PRINCESS	PLENTY	DOUBLE	£285	YELLOW	08/10/2005

Answer 20b

BED ORDERS : Table

MAKE	CUSTOMER	SIZE	PRICE	COLOUR	DELIVERY
SLEEPY	BROWN	KG	£445	PINK	02/09/2005
SNOOZY	HATCHETT	DB	£370	WHITE	23/08/2005
NIGHT-TIME	DROVER	SN	£105	GREEN	15/09/2005
LULLABY	SMALL	SN	£85	WHITE	10/09/2005
REST-EASY	TIVOTT	KG	£395	BEIGE	15/09/2005
ASLEEP	STONE	DB	£404	YELLOW	08/10/2005
CALM	WAKEFIELD	KG	£575	WHITE	07/09/2005
SLEEPWELL	CHARLETON	SN	£99	BEIGE	05/10/2005
SOFTNESS	MANN	SN	£103	WHITE	18/09/2005
PRINCE	BILLINGS	DB	£392	YELLOW	25/10/2005

Answer 20c

Early Kingsize : Select Query

MAKE	CUSTOMER	PRICE
SLEEPY	BROWN	£445
CALM	WAKEFIELD	£575

Answer   20d

Over £110 not green : Select Query		
MAKE	SIZE	DELIVERY
PRINCE	DB	25/10/2005
ASLEEP	DB	08/10/2005
REST-EASY	KG	15/09/2005
CALM	KG	07/09/2005
SLEEPY	KG	02/09/2005
SNOOZY	DB	23/08/2005

Answer   20e

Double in October : Select Query		
CUSTOMER	MAKE	PRICE
STONE	ASLEEP	£404
BILLINGS	PRINCE	£392

Answer   20f

Beds Over £110

MAKE	*SIZE*	*DELIVERY*
PRINCE	DB	25/10/2005
ASLEEP	DB	08/10/2005
REST-EASY	KG	15/09/2005
CALM	KG	07/09/2005
SLEEPY	KG	02/09/2005
SNOOZY	DB	23/08/2005

Exercise 21

Task 1

1. Open the database *Families* and the *Family Details* table.

2. Set the page to landscape orientation.

3. Print a copy of the table, displaying all records in full.

4. Close the table.

5. Rename it *Family Members*.

6. It will be quicker if your database uses codes for the TOWN field, so replace the existing entries as follows:

a) MANCHESTER becomes MCH.

b) TRURO becomes TRO.

c) WORCESTER becomes WOR.

d) LONDON becomes LON.

e) NORWICH becomes NCH.

f) BOURNEMOUTH becomes BTH.

g) WINDSOR becomes WIN.

7. Two more members of the family need to be added:

a) SELENA TWIST is 42, her shoe size is 7, she has BROWN eyes and her birthday is 13/9/1963. She lives in LONDON.

b) DAN PETERS is 65 and wears size 9 shoes. His eyes are BLUE and his birthday is on 3/5/1940. He lives in WINDSOR.

8. MAUREEN ELLIS moved away and contact was lost. Delete her record from the database.

9. There are a few errors to correct:

a) MARY HAVLOCK has GREEN eyes.

b) SANDRA BLYTHE's first name should be SANDIE.

c) PETER WINTHORP is 32 in age, and so his birthday is 2/11/1973.

10. Print the data in table format, ensuring it is fully displayed.

Task 2

11. You decide to invite all the younger family members to a party. Set up the following database query:

a) Find all the people who are under 25 years in AGE.

b) Sort them alphabetically by SURNAME.

c) Display only their FIRST NAME, SURNAME and TOWN.

d) Save the query as *Under 25* and print a copy in table format.

12. You now want to see how many relatives have the same eye colour and similar shoe size to yourself. Set up the following query:

a) Find everyone who has BROWN EYE COLOUR and whose SHOE SIZE is between 6 and 8.

b) Sort the records in alphabetical order of TOWN.

c) Display the fields FIRST NAME, SURNAME, AGE and TOWN only.

d) Save the query as *Brown eyes small feet* and print a copy in table format.

Task 3

13. Finally, you want to find out who is over 50. Set up the following query:

   a) Find people with a BIRTHDAY earlier than 1955.

   b) Sort the records in descending order of BIRTHDAY.

   c) Display only the FIRST NAME, SURNAME, BIRTHDAY and TOWN.

   d) Save the query as *Over 50* and print a copy in table format.

Task 4

14. Using the query *Over 50*, create a report in portrait orientation.

15. Give the report the title: *People over 50*.

16. Save it as *Over 50 report*.

17. Print a copy, ensuring all data is fully displayed and that the automatic page number is visible in the footer.

18. Close the database file and exit the application.

Answer 21a

FAMILY DETAILS : Table

FIRST NAME	SURNAME	AGE	SHOE SIZE	EYE COLOUR	BIRTHDAY	TOWN
KEN	HAVLOCK	47	10	BLUE	12/09/1958	MANCHESTER
MARY	HAVLOCK	41	5	BROWN	23/07/1964	MANCHESTER
STEPHEN	HAVLOCK	10	5	BLUE	01/08/1995	MANCHESTER
PETER	WINTHORP	34	10	BROWN	02/11/1971	WORCESTER
HELEN	WINTHORP	30	6	GREY	15/06/1975	WORCESTER
DAISY	WINTHORP	5	2	BLUE	02/12/2000	WORCESTER
DONALD	WINTHORP	10	6	GREY	13/03/1995	WORCESTER
SANDRA	DELLAWARE	26	5	BLUE	14/05/1979	LONDON
MATTHEW	DELLAWARE	44	8	BROWN	28/09/1961	LONDON
MARILYN	PETERS	57	6	GREEN	02/02/1948	WINDSOR
BERTIE	BLYTHE	60	11	BROWN	30/07/1945	NORWICH
DIANA	BLYTHE	61	6	GREY	04/05/1944	NORWICH
SANDRA	BLYTHE	22	6	BROWN	16/04/1983	BOURNEMOUTH
MAUREEN	ELLIS	80	4	GREY	04/03/1925	TRURO

Answer 21b

FAMILY MEMBERS : Table

FIRST NAME	SURNAME	AGE	SHOE SIZE	EYE COLOUR	BIRTHDAY	TOWN
KEN	HAVLOCK	47	10	BLUE	12/09/1958	MCH
MARY	HAVLOCK	41	5	GREEN	23/07/1964	MCH
STEPHEN	HAVLOCK	10	5	BLUE	01/08/1995	MCH
PETER	WINTHORP	32	10	BROWN	02/11/1973	WOR
HELEN	WINTHORP	30	6	GREY	15/06/1975	WOR
DAISY	WINTHORP	5	2	BLUE	02/12/2000	WOR
DONALD	WINTHORP	10	6	GREY	13/03/1995	WOR
SANDRA	DELLAWARE	26	5	BLUE	14/05/1979	LON
MATTHEW	DELLAWARE	44	8	BROWN	28/09/1961	LON
MARILYN	PETERS	57	6	GREEN	02/02/1948	WIN
BERTIE	BLYTHE	60	11	BROWN	30/07/1945	NCH
DIANA	BLYTHE	61	6	GREY	04/05/1944	NCH
SANDIE	BLYTHE	22	6	BROWN	16/04/1983	BTH
SELENA	TWIST	42	7	BROWN	13/09/1963	LON
DAN	PETERS	65	9	BLUE	03/05/1940	WIN

Answer 21c

Under 25 : Select Query

FIRST NAME	SURNAME	TOWN
SANDIE	BLYTHE	BTH
STEPHEN	HAVLOCK	MCH
DONALD	WINTHORP	WOR
DAISY	WINTHORP	WOR

Answer 21d

Brown eyes small feet : Select Query

FIRST NAME	SURNAME	AGE	TOWN
SANDIE	BLYTHE	22	BTH
SELENA	TWIST	42	LON
MATTHEW	DELLAWARE	44	LON

Answer 21e

Over 50 : Select Query

FIRST NAME	SURNAME	BIRTHDAY	TOWN
MARILYN	PETERS	02/02/1948	WIN
BERTIE	BLYTHE	30/07/1945	NCH
DIANA	BLYTHE	04/05/1944	NCH
DAN	PETERS	03/05/1940	WIN

People over 50

FIRST NAME	SURNAME	BIRTHDAY	TOWN
MARILYN	PETERS	02/02/1948	WIN
BERTIE	BLYTHE	30/07/1945	NCH
DIANA	BLYTHE	04/05/1944	NCH
DAN	PETERS	03/05/1940	WIN

Exercise 22

Task 1

1. Open the database *Books on Tape* and the table *Tapes*.

2. Change to landscape orientation.

3. Print the records in table format.

4. Close the table.

5. Open and rename it *Cassettes*.

6. Using codes for the **CATEGORY** would be more efficient. Replace the existing entries as follows:

   a) Replace **CHILDREN** with **CH**.

   b) Replace **HISTORY** with **HY**.

   c) Replace **COMEDY** with **CO**.

   d) Replace **FICTION** with **FN**.

7. The tape by **ROBIN JARVIS** has been damaged. Delete the record from the database.

8. You have bought three new tapes. Add these to the table:

   a) **VICTORIA WOOD** with her **LIVE 1997** performance in the **CO** category lasts **80 MINS**. The tape cost **£9.99**, the publisher is **PUFFIN** and it came out in the year **1998**.

   b) **JULES VERNE** wrote **JOURNEY TO THE CENTRE OF THE EARTH** which was published on tape by **PENGUIN** in **1996**. The tape cost **£9.99**, is in the **FN** category and lasts **180 MINS**.

   c) **ANTHONY HOROWITZ** wrote **GRANNY** which was published by **BBC** in **2001**. It lasts **210 MINS** and cost **£12.50**. It is in the **CH** category.

9. Some of the information needs to be updated:

    a) The VICTORIA WOOD tape cost £11.50.

    b) THE WIND SINGER lasts 200 MINS.

10. Print all the data in table format, making sure all records are fully displayed.

Task 2

11. You want to see how many tapes you have that last under 3 hours. Set up the following query:

    a) Select all tapes with a TIME less than 180 MINS.

    b) Sort them in alphabetical order of TITLE.

    c) Display only AUTHOR, TITLE, CATEGORY and YEAR.

    d) Save the query as *Under 3 hours* and print it out in table format.

12. Now you want to find out which of the tapes are comedies that cost under £12. Set up the following query:

    a) Select all tapes in the CO category with a PRICE under £12.

    b) Display only the AUTHOR, TITLE, TIME and PRICE.

    c) Sort the records in descending order of PRICE.

    d) Save the query as *Comedies under £12* and print out the records in table format.

Task 3

13. Finally, you would like to know how many old fiction tapes you have. Set up the following query:

    a) Select all tapes in the FN category produced before the YEAR 2000.

    b) Display only the TITLE, PRICE and PUBLISHER fields.

    c) Sort the records in alphabetical order of PUBLISHER.

    d) Save the query as *Fiction before 2000* and print the records in table format.

Task 4

14. Using the query *Under 3 hours*, create a report in portrait orientation.

15. Give the report the title: *Short tapes*.

16. Save the report as *Under 3 hour tapes*.

17. Print a copy of the report making sure the data is fully displayed.

18. Close the database and exit the application.

Answer 22a

TAPES : Table

AUTHOR/ARTIST	TITLE	CATEGORY	TIME(MINS)	PRICE	PUBLISHER	YEAR
WILLIAM NICHOLSON	THE WIND SINGER	CHILDREN	180	£12.99	COLLINS	1992
GOONS	WHAT TIME IS IT, ECCLES?	COMEDY	120	£12.00	BBC	2001
TONY ROBINSON	THESEUS	HISTORY	96	£9.99	CAVALCADE	1988
TERRY PRATCHETT	WINGS	FICTION	180	£12.99	CORGI	1993
TERRY PRATCHETT	TRUCKERS	FICTION	180	£12.99	CORGI	1993
GOONS	THE ELECTION	COMEDY	100	£5.50	BESPOKE AUDIO	1964
ROWAN ATKINSON	WEDDING	COMEDY	90	£6.99	LAUGHING STOCK	1995
ANDREW SACHS	GREEK MYTHS	HISTORY	165	£10.50	CAVALCADE	1992
MICHAEL MORPURGO	KENSUKE'S KINGDOM	CHILDREN	120	£12.50	COLLINS	2001
ROBIN JARVIS	THORN OGRES	CHILDREN	210	£16.99	PENGUIN	1999

Answer 22b

CASSETTES : Table

AUTHOR/ARTIST	TITLE	CATEGORY	TIME(MINS)	PRICE	PUBLISHER	YEAR
WILLIAM NICHOLSON	THE WIND SINGER	CH	200	£12.99	COLLINS	1992
GOONS	WHAT TIME IS IT, ECCLES?	CO	120	£12.00	BBC	2001
TONY ROBINSON	THESEUS	HY	96	£9.99	CAVALCADE	1988
TERRY PRATCHETT	WINGS	FN	180	£12.99	CORGI	1993
TERRY PRATCHETT	TRUCKERS	FN	180	£12.99	CORGI	1993
GOONS	THE ELECTION	CO	100	£5.50	BESPOKE AUDIO	1964
ROWAN ATKINSON	WEDDING	CO	90	£6.99	LAUGHING STOCK	1995
ANDREW SACHS	GREEK MYTHS	HY	165	£10.50	CAVALCADE	1992
MICHAEL MORPURGO	KENSUKE'S KINGDOM	CH	120	£12.50	COLLINS	2001
VICTORIA WOOD	LIVE 1997	CO	80	£11.50	PUFFIN	1998
JULES VERNE	JOURNEY TO THE CENTRE (	FN	180	£9.99	PENGUIN	1996
ANTHONY HOROWITZ	GRANNY	CH	210	£12.50	BBC	2001

Answer 22c

under 3 hours : Select Query

AUTHOR/ARTIST	TITLE	CATEGORY	YEAR
ANDREW SACHS	GREEK MYTHS	HY	1992
MICHAEL MORPURGO	KENSUKE'S KINGDOM	CH	2001
VICTORIA WOOD	LIVE 1997	CO	1998
GOONS	THE ELECTION	CO	1964
TONY ROBINSON	THESEUS	HY	1988
ROWAN ATKINSON	WEDDING	CO	1995
GOONS	WHAT TIME IS IT, ECCLES?	CO	2001
			0

Record: 7 of 7

Answer 22d

comedies under £12 : Select Query

AUTHOR/ARTIST	TITLE	TIME(MINS)	PRICE
VICTORIA WOOD	LIVE 1997	80	£11.50
ROWAN ATKINSON	WEDDING	90	£6.99
GOONS	THE ELECTION	100	£5.50
		0	£0.00

Record: 4 of 4

UNIT 3: DATABASE MANIPULATION **113**

Answer   22e

Microsoft Access - [fiction before 2000 : Select Query]

File Edit View Insert Format Records Tools Window Help

TITLE	PRICE	PUBLISHER
WINGS	£12.99	CORGI
TRUCKERS	£12.99	CORGI
JOURNEY TO THE CENTRE OF THE EARTH	£9.99	PENGUIN
	£0.00	

Record: 1 of 3

Datasheet View   NUM

Answer   22f

short tapes

AUTHOR/ARTIST	TITLE	CATEGORY	YEAR
ANDREW SACHS	GREEK MYTHS	HY	1992
MICHAEL MORPURGO	KENSUKE'S KINGDOM	CH	2001
VICTORIA WOOD	LIVE 1997	CO	1998
GOONS	THE ELECTION	CO	1964
TONY ROBINSON	THESEUS	HY	1988
ROWAN ATKINSON	WEDDING	CO	1995
GOONS	WHAT TIME IS IT, ECCLES?	CO	2001

UNIT **4**

Producing an e-publication

For this unit, you must be able to use appropriate software to create a one-page newsletter displaying a heading, columns of text and an image that is laid out exactly as specified.

EXERCISES 1, 2 AND 3

Test your ability to:

▶ Start a new publication

▶ Add text frames and enter text

▶ Use different font sizes

▶ Save a publication

▶ Close a publication

Assessment Objectives: 1c, 1f, 4a and 4b

Exercise 1

1. Open the appropriate software.

2. Start a new publication.

3. Enter the following text as a heading at the top of the page: LOSE WEIGHT AND KEEP FIT. Increase its size so that it is clearly visible.

4. Now create a second frame and enter the following main text:

   If you want to lose weight and have fun, come along to our Work-It-Out Club every Tuesday and attend a family fitness class.

5. Make sure this text is a different size to the heading.

6. Save as *Fitness*.

7. Close the publication.

LOSE WEIGHT AND KEEP
FIT

If you want to lose weight
and have fun, come along to
our Work-It-Out Club every
Tuesday and attend a family
fitness class.

Exercise 2   1.   Start a new publication.

2.   Enter the following text as a heading: SCHOOL UNIFORM. Increase the font size so the text is clearly visible and it fills most of the width of the page.

3.   Create a second frame and enter the following main text in a smaller font size: Save money and buy your child's uniform second-hand.

4.   Save as *School*.

5.   Close the publication.

Answer

SCHOOL UNIFORM

Save money and buy your
child's uniform second-hand.

Exercise 3 1. Start a new publication.

2. Enter the following text as a heading: **CHRISTMAS PANTOMIME**. Increase the font size so the text is clearly visible and it fills most of the width of the page.

3. Create a second frame and enter the following main text in a smaller font size: **We proudly present Mother Goose which will be shown at the Town Hall every evening from 22–29 December at 7.30 p.m.**

4. Save as *Panto*.

5. Close the publication.

Answer

CHRISTMAS PANTOMIME

We proudly present Mother Goose
which will be shown at the Town
Hall every evening from 22–29 December at 7.30 p.m.

EXERCISES 4, 5 AND 6

Test your ability to:

◆ Import an image

◆ Place an image

◆ Manipulate an image

◆ Print the publication

Assessment Objectives: 2b, 2c, 3e and 4b

Exercise 4 **1.** Start a new publication.

2. Enter the following as a heading: PRESIDENT OF THE UNITED STATES OF AMERICA.

3. Create a second text frame and enter the following main text:

The President will be visiting the Guildhall on Saturday, 24 July at 2.00 p.m. where he will be presented with the keys to the city.

4. Format the heading so that it is clearly larger than the main text.

5. Insert the image *Keys* and position it in the bottom right-hand corner of the publication. Ensure that it does not obscure any text.

6. Save the publication as *President*.

7. Print a copy of the publication, making sure it fits one page.

8. Now reduce the image in size and move it to the top of the publication on the right-hand side. Position it below the heading but above the main text.

9. Save the amended publication and print one copy before closing the file.

Answer 4a

PRESIDENT OF THE UNITED
STATES OF AMERICA

The President will be visiting
the Guildhall on Saturday, 24
July at 2.00 p.m. where he will be
presented with the keys to the
city.

Answer 4b

PRESIDENT OF THE UNITED
STATES OF AMERICA

The President will be visiting
the Guildhall on Saturday, 24
July at 2.00 p.m. where he will be
presented with the keys to the
city.

Exercise 5 1. Start a new publication.

2. Enter the heading **NOTICE** at the top of the page formatted to a large font.

3. Under this, create a new text frame and enter the following text in a smaller font: During the summer period, our shop in Stairwell Road will be shut for the whole of August. During that time, please visit our Sheep Street branch and the staff will be happy to help you.

4. Import the image *Fan* and position this centrally at the bottom of the page.

5. Save as *Shop* and print one copy.

6. Now reduce the size of the image and move it to the bottom left-hand corner.

7. Save these changes and print a copy of the amended publication.

8. Close the file.

Answer 5a

NOTICE

During the summer period, our
shop in Stairwell Road will be
shut for the whole of August.
During that time, please visit
our Sheep Street branch and the
staff will be happy to help you.

Answer 5b

NOTICE

During the summer period, our
shop in Stairwell Road will be
shut for the whole of August.
During that time, please visit
our Sheep Street branch and the
staff will be happy to help you.

Exercise 6

1. Start a new publication.

2. Enter the following as a heading: CURLY CREATIONS.

3. Create a second text frame and enter the following main text:

   Michael Le Grand, hairdresser to the stars, is opening his new salon here on Saturday, 21 July. Call in for an appointment – the first 10 people will receive free shampoo.

4. Format the heading so that it is clearly larger than the main text.

5. Insert the image *Drier* and position it in the bottom left-hand corner of the publication. Ensure that it does not obscure any text.

6. Save the publication as *Haircut*.

7. Print a copy of the publication, making sure it fits one page.

8. Now move the image to the top of the publication on the left-hand side of the main text, below the heading.

9. Crop the image to remove the electric cord and plug.

10. Save the amended publication and print one copy before closing the file.

Answer 6a

CURLY CREATIONS

Michael Le Grand, hair-
dresser to the stars, is
opening his new salon here
on Saturday, 21 July. Call
in for an appointment – the
first 10 people will re-
ceive free shampoo.

```
┌─────────────────────────────────────┐
│                                     │
│      CURLY CREATIONS                │
│                                     │
│          Michael Le Grand,          │
│          hairdresser to the         │
│     stars, is opening his new       │
│     salon here on Saturday, 21      │
│     July.  Call in for an ap-       │
│     pointment – the first 10        │
│     people will receive free        │
│     shampoo.                        │
│                                     │
│                                     │
│                                     │
│                                     │
└─────────────────────────────────────┘
```

EXERCISES 7, 8 AND 9

Test your ability to:

◗ Use serif or sans serif fonts

◗ Align text

Assessment Objectives: 1e and 3a

Exercise 7 1. Start a new publication and enter the heading at the top of the page using a serif font: Creating Web Pages.

2. Increase the size of the heading text so that it extends across the full width of the page.

3. Centre the heading.

4. Below this, create a second frame and enter the following text using a sans serif font: If you run your own business, want to sell home-made sweets or cakes, or simply like the idea of being online, it is very easy to create your very own Home Page.

5. Increase the size of the text so that it is clearly visible but smaller than the heading text.

6. Import the image *Cake* and resize it so that it is twice its original size.

7. Position it so that it fills the top left-hand corner of the main frame but does not obscure any text.

8. Save the publication as *Web page*.

9. Print one copy.

10. Now centre the main text.

11. Reduce the size of the image and move it to below the main text, in the bottom right-hand corner of the page.

12. Flip the image horizontally so that it is facing in the opposite direction.

13. Save these changes and print a copy of the amended publication before closing.

Answer 7a

Creating Web Pages

If you run your own business,
want to sell home-made sweets
or cakes, or simply like the idea
of being online, it is very easy to
create your very own Home
Page.

Exercise 8 1. Start a new publication and enter the heading at the top of the page using a sans serif font: FESTIVAL OF MUSIC.

2. Increase the size of the heading text so that it extends across the full width of the page.

3. Centre the heading.

4. Below this, create a second frame and enter the following text using a serif font: For music lovers everywhere, make sure you visit the Festival that will be taking place here next month.

5. Increase the size of the text so that it is clearly visible but smaller than the heading text.

6. Centre the main text.

7. Import the image *Guitar* and resize it so that it is twice its original size.

8. Position it so that it is centred in the bottom half of the publication but does not obscure any text.

9. Save the publication as *Music Festival*.

10. Print one copy.

11. Now reduce the size of the image and move it to the right of the main text, just below the heading.

12. Crop the picture to remove the neck of the guitar extending beyond the green background square.

13. Left-align the main text.

14. Save these changes and print a copy of the amended publication before closing.

Answer 8a

FESTIVAL OF MUSIC

For music lovers every-
where, make sure
you visit the Festi-
val that will be tak-
ing place here next month.

Exercise 9   1.   Start a new publication and enter the heading at the top of the page using a sans serif font: SAVE OUR CHURCH ORGAN.

2.   Increase the size of the heading text so that it extends across the full width of the page.

3.   Centre the heading.

4.   Below this, create a second frame and enter the following text using a serif font: Concerts, a 10-mile walk and other activities are all being organized to raise money – so please give generously.

5.   Increase the size of the text so that it is clearly visible but smaller than the heading text.

6.   Import the image *Church* and resize it so that it is twice its original size.

7.   Position it so that it is centred at the bottom of the publication but does not obscure any text.

8.   Save the publication as *Organ*.

9.   Print one copy.

10. Now reduce the size of the image and move it to the left of the main text, just below the heading.

11. Centre the main text.

12. Save these changes and print a copy of the amended publication before closing.

Answer 9a

SAVE OUR CHURCH ORGAN

Concerts, a 10-mile walk and other activities are all being organized to raise money – so please give generously.

Answer 9b

SAVE OUR CHURCH ORGAN

Concerts, a 10-mile walk and other activities are all being organized to raise money – so please give generously.

Test your ability to:

◆ Set page size/orientation

◆ Set page margins

◆ Use lines and borders

Assessment Objectives: 1a, 1b and 2e

Exercise 10

1. Start a new publication in landscape orientation.

2. Set the top, bottom, left and right margins to 3 cm.

3. Enter the heading WRITING GOOD ENGLISH using a sans serif font.

4. Increase the size of the heading text so that it extends across the full width of the page.

5. Centre the heading.

6. Now create a second text frame and position it below the heading. Enter the following text using a serif font: When we speak, we use punctuation by pausing, to help our listeners understand what we are saying. We also give other clues through our facial expressions, emphasis or tone. Punctuation is simply writing in these clues to help our readers.

7. Right-align this text and increase the font size, making sure it is still smaller than the heading text.

8. Add a final frame at the bottom of the page and enter the following text using a serif font: Find out more at our next English workshop, 25 June 6–9 p.m.

9. Format the text so that it is centre aligned and clearly larger than the main text but smaller than the heading text.

10. Insert the image *Writing* into the main frame, just below the heading on the right. Make sure it does not obscure any text.

11. Save the publication as *English* and print one copy.

12. Now reduce the size of the image and position it in the bottom left-hand corner of the publication, making sure it does not obscure any text.

13. Draw a thick line below the heading to separate it from the main text.

14. Save these changes and print a copy of the amended publication.

15. Close the file.

Answer 10a

WRITING GOOD ENGLISH

When we speak, we use punctuation by pausing, to help our listeners under-stand what we are saying. We also give other clues through our facial expres-sions, emphasis or tone. Punctuation is simply writing in these clues to help our readers.

Find out more at our next English workshop, 25 June 6–9 p.m.

Answer 10b

WRITING GOOD ENGLISH

When we speak, we use punctuation by pausing, to help our listeners understand what we are saying. We also give other clues through our facial expressions, emphasis or tone. Punctuation is simply writing in these clues to help our readers.

Find out more at our next English workshop, 25 June 6 – 9 pm

Exercise 11

1. Start a new publication in portrait orientation.

2. Set the left and right margins to 3.5 cm and top and bottom margins to 2 cm.

3. Enter the heading Healthy Lifestyle at the top of the page using a serif font.

4. Increase the size of the text so that it extends the full width of the publication.

5. Create a main text frame and enter the following text using a sans serif font:

    What We Want

    We all want to be fit and healthy, and it is not too difficult to stay that way.

    What To Do

    Here are 3 golden rules for living a full life: do not smoke, do not drink to excess and try to eat five fruits or vegetables a day.

6. Increase the font size so that it fills most of the page but is not as large as the heading text.

7. Insert the image *Exercise* and position it in the bottom right-hand corner of the publication.

8. Save the publication as *Health* and print one copy.

9. Increase the size of the subheadings What We Want and What To Do so that they are larger than the main text but smaller than the heading text.

10. Reduce the size of the image and move it into the main frame so that it is to the left of the first subheading and does not obscure any text.

11. Draw a border round the heading to separate it from the main text.

12. Save these changes and print a copy of the amended publication.

13. Close the file.

Answer   11a

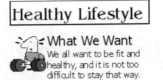

Healthy Lifestyle

What We Want
We all want to be fit and healthy, and it is not too difficult to stay that way.

What To Do
Here are 3 golden rules for living a full life: do not smoke, do not drink to excess and try to eat five fruits or vegetables a day.

4

Exercise 12

1. Start a new publication in landscape orientation.

2. Set the top, bottom, left and right margins to 2.5 cm.

3. Enter the heading SANTA'S GROTTO using a sans serif font.

4. Increase the size of the heading text so that it extends across the full width of the page.

5. Centre the heading.

6. Now create a second text frame and position it below the heading. Enter the following text using a serif font: Now that it is nearly Christmas, we want to welcome you to Santa's Grotto in the centre of Hazeldean. Come along any day between 10 and 3 to meet Santa and receive a gift.

7. Right-align this text and increase the font size, making sure it is still smaller than the heading text.

8. Add a final frame at the bottom of the page and enter the following text using a serif font: Tickets available in the Library.

9. Format the text so that it is centre aligned and clearly larger than the main text but smaller than the heading text.

10. Insert the image *Santa* into the main frame, just below the heading on the left. Make sure it does not obscure any text.

11. Save the publication as *Grotto* and print one copy.

12. Now reduce the size of the image and position it in the bottom right-hand corner of the publication, making sure it does not obscure any text.

13. Draw a thick line below the heading to separate it from the main text.

14. Save these changes and print a copy of the amended publication.

15. Close the file.

Answer 12a

SANTA'S GROTTO

Now that it is nearly Christmas, we want to welcome you to Santa's Grotto in the centre of Hazeldean. Come along any day between 10 and 3 to meet Santa and receive a gift.

Tickets available in the Library

Answer 12b

SANTA'S GROTTO

Now that it is nearly Christmas, we want to welcome you to Santa's Grotto in the centre of Hazeldean. Come along any day between 10 and 3 to meet Santa and receive a gift.

Tickets available in the Library

EXERCISES 13, 14 AND 15

Test your ability to:

▶ Import a text file

▶ Place text as specified

▶ Set column widths and spacing

▶ Justify text

▶ Use the spell checker

Assessment Objectives: 1d, 2a, 2d, 3a and 3d

Exercise 13
1. Start a new publication.

2. Set the page to landscape orientation and set the left and right margins to 3 cm.

3. Set up the page layout to include a page wide heading and 2 columns of text. Set the column widths as equal with a space between the columns of 2 cm.

4. Enter the following heading using a serif font: The History of Henry VIII.

5. Increase the size of the heading text so that it extends across the full width of both columns.

6. Import the text file *Henry* so that it begins at the top of the left-hand column just below the heading.

7. Proof read and correct the 3 spelling errors.

8. Format the text to be left aligned in a sans serif font.

9. Import the image file *Kings* and position it within the first column, at the bottom of the page. Make sure it does not obscure any text.

10. Save the publication as *History of Henry*.

11. Print a copy, making sure it fits on one page.

12. Now reduce the size of the image and move it to the top of the second column.

13. Draw a border round the heading to separate it from the main text.

14. Increase the size of the subheadings The Throne, Enemies and Marriage so that they are larger than the body text but smaller than the heading text.

15. Change the main text to fully justified.

16. Increase the size of the main text so that it extends well into the second column, whilst still retaining the heading, subheading and main text as different sizes.

17. Save these changes and print a copy of the amended publication.

18. Close the file.

Text to *Henry* file

The Throne

Henry VIII was bron at Greenwich on 28 June 1491, the second son of Henry VII and Elizabeth of York. He became heir to the throne on the death of his elder brother, Prince Arthur, in 1502 and succeeded in 1509. He was a scholar and well educated, speaking grood French, Latin and Spanish. He was also very religious, often attending three masses a day. An athletic man, he was partial to a gamme of tennis and regularly went hunting.

Enemies

Henry enjoyed writing and was known for both books and music. He was a lavish patron of the arts and his many interests meant he did not take as much time over governmental or administrative business as his colleagues might have wished. It allowed people such as Thomas Wolsey to increase their own influence in his many absences. In fact, Wolsey became Lord Chancellor in 1515 and was so powerful a minister he was able to build Hampton Court Palace which turned out to be a building on a grander scale than anything owned by the king himself.

Marriage

We all know Henry VIII as a tyrannical monster, but he made himself a dominant figure in Europe and inspired fear and devotion equally in his subjects. Best known for his many marriages, it was the need to secure the succession to the throne that led to his later marriages, although it was his passion for Anne Boleyn that led to his divorce from Catherine of Aragon and the severance from Rome which is the outstanding event of his reign.

Answer 13a

The History of Henry VIII

The Throne
Henry VIII was born at Greenwich on 28 June 1491, the second son of Henry VII and Elizabeth of York. He became heir to the throne on the death of his elder brother, Prince Arthur, in 1502 and succeeded in 1509. He was a scholar and well educated, speaking good French, Latin and Spanish. He was also very religious, often attending three masses a day. An athletic man, he was partial to a game of tennis and regularly went hunting.

Enemies
Henry enjoyed writing and was know for both books and music. He was a lavish patron of the arts and his many interests meant he did not take as much time over governmental or administrative business as his colleagues might have wished. It allowed people such as Thomas Wolsey to increase their own influence in his many absences. In fact, Wolsey became Lord Chancellor in 1515 and was so powerful a minister, he was able to build Hampton Court Palace which turned out to be a building on a grander scale than anything owned by the king himself.

Marriage
We all know Henry VIII as a tyrannical monster, but he made himself a dominant figure in Europe and inspired fear and devotion equally in his subjects. Best known for his many marriages, it was the need to secure the succession to the throne that led to his later marriages, although it was his passion for Anne Boleyn that led to his divorce from Catherine of Aragon and the severance from Rome which is the outstanding event of his reign.

Answer 13b

The History of Henry VIII

The Throne
Henry VIII was born at Greenwich on 28 June 1491, the second son of Henry VII and Elizabeth of York. He became heir to the throne on the death of his elder brother, Prince Arthur, in 1502 and succeeded in 1509. He was a scholar and well educated, speaking good French, Latin and Spanish. He was also very religious, often attending three masses a day. An athletic man, he was partial to a game of tennis and regularly went hunting.

Enemies
Henry enjoyed writing and was know for both books and music. He was a lavish patron of the arts and his many interests meant he did not take as much time over governmental or administrative business as his colleagues might have wished. It allowed people such as Thomas Wolsey to increase their own influence in his many absences. In fact, Wolsey became Lord Chancellor in 1515 and was so powerful a minister,

he was able to build Hampton Court Palace which turned out to be a building on a grander scale than anything owned by the king himself.

Marriage
We all know Henry VIII as a tyrannical monster, but he made himself a dominant figure in Europe and inspired fear and devotion equally in his subjects. Best known for his many marriages, it was the need to secure the succession to the throne that led to his later marriages, although it was his passion for Anne Boleyn that led to his divorce from Catherine of Aragon and the severance from Rome which is the outstanding event of his reign.

Exercise 14

1. Start a new publication.

2. Set the page to portrait orientation and set the left and right margins to 3.5 cm and the top and bottom margins to 2 cm.

3. Set up the page layout to include a page-wide heading and 2 columns of text. Set the column widths as equal with a space between the columns of 1.5 cm.

4. Enter the following heading using a serif font: John Constable.

5. Increase the size of the heading text so that it extends across the full width of both columns.

6. Import the text file *Constable* so that it begins at the top of the left-hand column below the heading.

7. Spell check and correct the 3 spelling mistakes.

8. Format the text to be left aligned in a sans serif font.

9. Import the image file *Landscape* and position it within the first column, at the top of the page just above the first subheading. Make sure it does not obscure any text.

10. Save the publication as *Constable*.

11. Print a copy, making sure it fits on one page.

12. Now reduce the size of the image and move it to the top of the second column.

13. Draw a thick line below the heading to separate it from the main text.

14. Increase the size of the subheadings John Constable, Suffolk, Wiltshire and Other Counties so that they are larger than the body text but smaller than the heading text.

15. Change the main text to fully justified.

16. Increase the size of the main text so that it partially fills the second column, whilst still retaining the heading, subheading and main text as different sizes.

17. Save these changes and print a copy of the amended publication.

18. Close the file.

Text of *Constable* file

John Constable

English Romantic art will always be associated with two artists, Joseph Turner and John Constable. Constable was without doubt one of the great British landscape artists of the eighteenth century. He depicted the truth as he sar it, representing in paint the atmospheric effects of changing light in the open air, the beauty of trees through the seasons and the movement of clouds across the sky. Today we can visit the places that Constable painted and, quite often, see the same or similar scenes that inspired him all those years ago.

Suffolk

One such place is Dedham, in Suffolk. Here he painted The Hay Wain and Willy Lot's Cottage, and this actyal building is now part of an educational centre that provides courses in painting as well as natural history. He particularly loved the views across the countryside near Dedham and along the River Stour.

Wiltshire

His largest watercolour was of a most famous landmark, Stonehenge, and the painting can be viewed at the Salisbury and South Wiltshire Museum. In the same area, he pailted Salisbury Cathedral from the Meadows and Salisbury Cathedral from the Bishop's Grounds.

Other Counties

Constable painted in some surprising places and it is interesting to note that these included Brighton Beach which is not normally associated with the painter. In the same way, Essex and Cambridgeshire both inspired him to paint many landscapes including Hadleigh Castle.

4

JOHN CONSTABLE

the painting can be viewed at the Salisbury and South Wiltshire Museum. In the same area, he painted Salisbury Cathedral from the Meadows and Salisbury Cathedral from the Bishop's Grounds.
Other Counties
Constable painted in some surprising places and it is interesting to note that these included Brighton Beach which is not normally associated with the painter. In the same way, Essex and Cambridgeshire both inspired him to paint many landscapes including Hadleigh Castle.

John Constable
English Romantic art will always be associated with two artists, Joseph Turner and John Constable. Constable was without doubt one of the great British landscape artists of the eighteenth century. He depicted the truth as he saw it, representing in paint the atmospheric effects of changing light in the open air, the beauty of trees through the seasons and the movement of clouds across the sky. Today we can visit the places that Constable painted and, quite often, see the same or similar scenes that inspired him all those years ago.
Suffolk
One such place is Dedham, in Suffolk. Here he painted The Hay Wain and Willy Lot's Cottage, and this actual building is now part of an educational centre that provides courses in painting as well as natural history. He particularly loved the views across the countryside near Dedham and along the River Stour.
Wiltshire
His largest watercolour was of a most famous landmark, Stonehenge, and

JOHN CONSTABLE

John Constable

English Romantic art will always be associated with two artists, Joseph Turner and John Constable. Constable was without doubt one of the great British landscape artists of the eighteenth century. He depicted the truth as he saw it, representing in paint the atmospheric effects of changing light in the open air, the beauty of trees through the seasons and the movement of clouds across the sky. Today we can visit the places that Constable painted and, quite often, see the same or similar scenes that inspired him all those years ago.

Suffolk

One such place is Dedham, in Suffolk. Here he painted The Hay Wain and Willy Lot's Cottage, and this actual building is now part of an educational centre that provides courses in painting as well as natural history. He particularly loved the views across the countryside near Dedham and along the River Stour.

Wiltshire

His largest watercolour was of a most famous landmark, Stonehenge, and the painting can be viewed at the Salisbury and South Wiltshire Museum. In the same area, he painted Salisbury Cathedral from the Meadows and Salisbury Cathedral from the Bishop's Grounds.

Other Counties

Constable painted in some surprising places and it is interesting to note that these included Brighton Beach which is not normally associated with the painter. In the same way, Essex and Cambridgeshire both inspired him to paint many landscapes including Hadleigh Castle.

Exercise 15

1. Start a new publication.

2. Set the page to landscape orientation and set the left and right margins to 3.5 cm.

3. Set up the page layout to include a page-wide heading and 2 columns of text. Set the column widths as equal with a space between the columns of 1.75 cm.

4. Enter the following heading using a serif font: VISITING LONDON.

5. Increase the size of the heading text so that it extends across the full width of both columns.

6. Import the text file *London* so that it begins at the top of the left-hand column just below the heading.

7. Spell check and correct any errors.

8. Format the text to be left aligned in a sans serif font.

9. Import the image file *Beefeater* and position it within the first column, at the bottom of the page. Make sure it does not obscure any text.

10. Save the publication as *London*.

11. Print a copy, making sure it fits on one page.

12. Now reduce the size of the image and move it to the top of the second column.

13. Draw a border round the heading to separate it from the main text.

14. Increase the size of the subheadings London Eye, Theatres and Tate Modern so that they are larger than the body text but smaller than the heading text.

15. Change the main text to fully justified.

16. Increase the size of the main text so that it extends well into the second column, whilst still retaining the heading, subheading and main text as different sizes.

17. Save these changes and print a copy of the amended publication.

18. Close the file.

Text of *London* file

There are so many places to visit in London that it can be difficult for the tourist with only a few days available to decide where to go. Here are just some of the many ways you can spend time in London which are well worth a detour.

London Eye

This is a marvellous priece of engineering, and the managers have made great efforts to minimize the unpleasantness of waiting to board. You can buy your tickets online and then use a simple machine to access the piece of paper you need. There is then a snaking waiting area which is partly under cover, in case it rains. Usually the wait is only 30 minutes or so, and as the queue slowly shuffles forward, you can see how near you are to the end of the line. When you finally arrive, the cars you travel on gently pass the platform, opening with enough time for even disabled passengers to get on before you are taken slowly up in an arc. Take your camera with you in case you want a lasting image of the Houses of Parliament and the River Thames.

Theatres

No-one should ever visik London without booking a seat at one of the many theatres in the capital. The choice is so wide – from Shakespeare to musical – that any taste will be catered for. Our British stage actors are the best in the world, and you may even catch the odd American including Kevin Spacey now settled at the Old Vic.

Tate Modern

This wonderful old building on the Thames houses some of the most exciting modern art you will ever find. The great entrance hall usually has a set piece such as a giant spider or sound installation, and you can then travel upwards thrugh time to find paintings and sculpture by any artist you could name. The café is well worth a stop too, as you will find lovely sandwiches and excellent coffee.

Answer   15a

VISITING LONDON

There are so many places to visit in London that it can be difficult for the tourist with only a few days available to decide where to go. Here are just some of the many ways you can spend time in London which are well worth a detour.

London Eye

This is a marvellous piece of engineering, and the managers have made great efforts to minimise the unpleasantness of waiting to board. You can buy your tickets online and then use a simple machine to access the piece of paper you need. There is then a snaking waiting area which is partly under cover, in case it rains. Usually the wait is only 30 minutes or so, and as the queue slowly shuffles forward, you can see how near you are to the end of the line. When you finally arrive, the cars you travel on gently pass the platform, opening with enough time for even disabled passengers to get on before you are taken slowly up in an arc. Take your camera with you in case you want a lasting image of the Houses of Parliament and the River Thames.

Theatres

No-one should ever visit London without booking a seat at one of the many theatres in the capital. The

choice is so wide – from Shakespeare to musical – that any taste will be catered for. Our British stage actors are the best in the world, and you may even catch the odd American including Kevin Spacey now settled at the Old Vic.

Tate Modern

This wonderful old building on the Thames houses some of the most exciting modern art you will ever find. The great entrance hall usually has a set piece such as a giant spider or sound installation, and you can then travel upwards through time to find paintings and sculpture by any artist you could name. The café is well worth a stop too, as you will find lovely sandwiches and excellent coffee.

4

EXERCISES 16 AND 17

Test your ability to:

▶ Amend text

▶ Resize text to balance columns

Assessment Objectives: 3b and 3c

Exercise 16

1. Open the publication *History of Henry*.

2. Adjust the size of the text so that the columns are balanced at the bottom of the page. Make sure the heading, subheading and body text are still different sizes.

3. Change the subheading Enemies to Interests.

4. Save these changes and print a copy of the publication.

5. Apply a first line indent to all paragraphs but do not save this change.

6. Close the file.

The History of Henry VIII

The Throne

Henry VIII was born at Greenwich on 28 June 1491, the second son of Henry VII and Elizabeth of York. He became heir to the throne on the death of his elder brother, Prince Arthur, in 1502 and succeeded in 1509. He was a scholar and well educated, speaking good French, Latin and Spanish. He was also very religious, often attending three masses a day. An athletic man, he was partial to a game of tennis and regularly went hunting.

Enemies

Henry enjoyed writing and was know for both books and music. He was a lavish patron of the arts and his many interests meant he did not take as much time over governmental or administrative business as his colleagues might have wished. It allowed people such as Thomas Wolsey to increase their own influence in his many absences. In fact, Wolsey became Lord

Chancellor in 1515 and was so powerful a minister, he was able to build Hampton Court Palace which turned out to be a building on a grander scale than anything owned by the king himself.

Marriage

We all know Henry VIII as a tyrannical monster, but he made himself a dominant figure in Europe and inspired fear and devotion equally in his subjects. Best known for his many marriages, it was the need to secure the succession to the throne that led to his later marriages, although it was his passion for Anne Boleyn that led to his divorce from Catherine of Aragon and the severance from Rome which is the outstanding event of his reign.

Exercise 17

1. Create a new publication.

2. Set the page to portrait orientation.

3. Set top and bottom margins to 2 cm and left and right margins to 3 cm.

4. Set up the layout in newsletter format, to include a page-wide heading above two columns of text. The columns should be equal with 1.5 cm spacing.

5. Add your name in the top margin.

6. Enter the heading STAYING ALIVE at the top of the page using a serif font.

7. Increase the size of the text so that it extends across the full width of both columns of text.

8. Import the text file *Survival Kit* so that it begins at the top of the left-hand column below the main heading.

9. Format the text to be fully justified, in a sans serif font.

10. Import the image *Camp* and place it within the first column, in the centre of the page, making sure it does not cover any text.

11. Draw a thick line vertically between the two columns, making sure no text is obscured.

12. Increase the size of the subheadings Survival Kit, Water and Food so that they are larger than the main text but smaller than the heading text.

13. Change the subheading Water to Finding Water.

14. Adjust the size of the text so that the columns are balanced at the bottom of the page. Make sure the different text sizes are maintained.

15. Save the publication as *Survival* and print a copy that fits on one page.

16. Close the publication.

Text of *Survival Kit* file

Survival Kit

If you go on any trip that has risks, it is very important to have with you a survival kit that will ensure your survival. Some of the basics that you must always carry include matches, candles, a compass, medical kit, knives, solid fuel tablets and a cooking/eating tin.

Water

Although we can live for some time without food, it is hard to survive for more than a couple of days without water. Try to cut down on water loss by avoiding exertion, don't lie on hot ground, eat as little as possible so you are not using up digestive juices, and don't talk. Finding water is not so difficult if you remember about condensation – tie plastic bags around leafy branches and you will soon collect moisture. You can also dig a hole and suspend a sheet of plastic in it, with a container underneath to catch the drops that condense on the underside.

Food

A healthy body can survive on reserves stored in its tissues, but you will need food for heat and energy and to recover after hard work. The main foods are carbohydrates such as sugars and starches; proteins from meat, fish and eggs; fats found mainly in animals and fish but which will require water for proper digestion; minerals such as phosphorus, calcium and magnesium; and vitamins including C, A and D.

Answer

My name

STAYING ALIVE

Survival Kit

If you go on any trip that has risks, it is very important to have with you a survival kit that will ensure your survival. Some of the basics that you must always carry include matches, candles, a compass, medical kit, knives, solid fuel tablets and a cooking/eating tin.

Finding Water

Although we can live for some time without food, it is hard to survive for more than a couple of days without water. Try to cut down on water loss by avoiding exertion, don't lie on hot ground, eat as little as possible so you are not using up digestive juices, and don't talk. Finding water is not so difficult if you remember about condensation – tie plastic bags around leafy branches and you will soon collect moisture. You can also dig a hole and suspend a sheet of plastic in it, with a container underneath to catch the drops that condense on the underside.

Food

A healthy body can survive on reserves stored in its tissues, but you will need food for heat and energy and to recover after hard work. The main foods are carbohydrates such as sugars and starches; proteins from meat, fish and eggs; fats found mainly in animals and fish but which will require water for proper digestion; minerals such as phosphorus, calcium and magnesium; and vitamins including C, A and D.

FULL ASSIGNMENTS – PRODUCING AN E-PUBLICATION

Exercise 18

Task 1

1. Create a new single-page publication.

2. Set up the master page/template as follows:

   a) A4 paper size

   b) Portrait orientation

   c) Left, right, top and bottom margins 2 cm.

3. Key in the date in the bottom margin.

4. Set up the layout in a newsletter format, to include a page-wide heading above two columns of text.

   a) Column widths equal

   b) Space between 1 cm.

5. Enter a heading **NEW BUILDING** at the top of the page in a serif font.

6. Increase the size of the heading text so that it extends across the full width of both columns of text.

7. Save this publication with the file name *New Build*.

Task 2

8. Import the text file *Trees* so that it begins at the top of the left-hand column, below the heading.

9. Spell check the text and correct the three errors.

10. Format the body text to be left aligned, in a sans serif font.

11. Import the image *Tree* and place it within the first column, at the bottom of the page, making sure it does not cover any text.

12. Make sure your publication fits onto one page.

13. Save the publication with the same name and print a composite proof copy.

Task 3

14. Now draw a border round the heading to separate it from the two columns. Make sure the border does not overlap any text.

15. Increase the size of the subheadings Grand Opening, Research Centres and Plaque so that they are larger than the body text but smaller than the heading text.

16. Make the image smaller and move it to the top of the second column. Make sure it does not extend into the margin.

17. Flip the image horizontally.

18. Change the subheading Plaque to Commemoration.

19. Change the body text to fully justified.

20. Save as *New Build 2*.

Task 4

21. Format the body text so that there is a space in front of the second and final subheadings.

22. Adjust the size of the text so that the columns are balanced at the bottom of the page. Make sure the heading, subheadings and body text are still different sizes.

23. Make sure your publication fits onto one page.

24. Save and print the publication.

25. Close the publication.

Text of *Trees* file

Grand Opening

The new Vice President of Allied Arboreal Ltd, Spencer Grange Jnr, made a special visit to London last week to open the new research building. This was the latest centre the company have commissioned, set in the leafy green suburbs of Acton. Mr Grange opened the proceedings byt describing the history of the company. He told his audience about the idea his father, Spencer Grange Snr, and a friend, Alfred Mollins, had of creating beautiful avenues and parks full of trees all over America and Europe. They started with a small oak wood in Ohio and then bought up land across the South until they now have 25 arboreta across the USA.

Research Centres

In 1995, they shet up their first research centre in Washington where they pioneered tree cultivation and investigated new methods of tree propagation, and since then opened four more in Canada and France before building the present site in England.

Marian Fairly, Head of Research, thanked the Vice President for attending the opening and then handed over the scissors so that the red tape across the entrance could be cut and everyone could proceed into the foyer.

Plaque

A plaqua commemorating the founding of the company was then unveiled before everyone joined staff in the dining hall for drinks and canapés. Some members of the audience then took a guided tour of the buildings and walked the famous tree avenue before leaving.

Answer   18a

NEW BUILDING

Grand Opening
The new Vice President of Allied Arboreal Ltd, Spencer Grange Jnr. made a special visit to London last week to open the new research building. This was the latest centre the company have commissioned, set in the leafy green suburbs of Acton.

Mr Grange opened the proceedings by describing the history of the company. He told his audience about the idea his father, Spencer Grange Snr, and a friend Alfred Mollins had of creating beautiful avenues and parks full of trees all over America and Europe. They started with a small oak wood in Ohio and then bought up land across the South until they now have 25 Arboretums across the USA.

Research Centres
In 1995, they set up their first research centre in Washington where they pioneered tree cultivation and investigated new methods of tree propagation, and since then opened four more in Canada and France before building the present site in England.

Marian Fairly, Head of Research, thanked the Vice President for attending the opening and then handed over the scissors so that the red tape across the entrance could be cut and everyone could proceed into the foyer.

Plaque
A plaque commemorating the founding of the company was then unveiled before everyone joined staff in the dining hall for drinks and canapes. Some members of the audience then took a guided tour of the buildings and walked the famous tree avenue before leaving.

Answer   18b

NEW BUILDING

Grand Opening
The new Vice President of Allied Arboreal Ltd, Spencer Grange Jnr. made a special visit to London last week to open the new research building. This was the latest centre the company have commissioned, set in the leafy green suburbs of Acton.

Mr Grange opened the proceedings by describing the history of the company. He told his audience about the idea his father, Spencer Grange Snr, and a friend Alfred Mollins had of creating beautiful avenues and parks full of trees all over America and Europe. They started with a small oak wood in Ohio and then bought up land across the South until they now have 25 Arboretums across the USA.

Research Centres
In 1995, they set up their first research centre in Washington where they pioneered tree cultivation and investigated new methods of tree propagation, and since then opened four more in Canada and France before building the present site in England.

Marian Fairly, Head of Research, thanked the Vice President for attending the opening and then handed over the scissors so that the red tape across the entrance could be cut and everyone could proceed into the foyer.

Commemoration
A plaque commemorating the founding of the company was then unveiled before everyone joined staff in the dining hall for drinks and canapes. Some members of the audience then took a guided tour of the buildings and walked the famous tree avenue before leaving.

1/1985

4

Exercise 19

1. Create a new single-page publication.

2. Set up the master page/template as follows:

   a) A4 paper size

   b) Portrait orientation

   c) Left and right margins 3 cm, top and bottom margins 2.5 cm.

3. Add your name in the bottom margin.

4. Set up the layout in a newsletter format, to include a page-wide heading above two columns of text.

   d) Column widths equal

   e) Space between 1.5 cm.

5. Enter a heading ANTIQUES FAIR at the top of the page in a serif font.

6. Increase the size of the heading text so that it extends across the full width of both columns of text.

7. Save this publication as *Antiques1*.

Task 2

8. Import the text file *Antiques* so that it begins at the top of the left-hand column, below the heading.

9. Format the body text to be left aligned, in a sans serif font.

10. Spell check and correct the three spelling errors.

11. Import the image *Cabinet* and place it within the first column, at the bottom of the page, making sure it does not cover any text.

12. Make sure your publication fits onto one page.

13. Save the publication with the original file name and print a composite proof copy.

Task 3

14. Now draw a line under the heading to separate it from the two columns. Make sure the line extends to both left and right margins and does not overlap any text.

15. Increase the size of the subheadings Company, Venues and Television so that they are larger than the body text but smaller than the heading text.

16. Crop the image to remove the lower legs and floor.

17. Make the image smaller and move it to the middle of the second column. Make sure it does not extend into the margin.

18. Change the wording of the subheading Television to Roadshow.

19. Save the publication as *Antiques 2*.

Task 4

20. Change the body text to fully justified.

21. Adjust the size of the text so that the columns are balanced at the bottom of the page. Make sure the heading, subheadings and body text are still different sizes.

22. Make sure your printed publication fits onto one page. Save and print the publication.

23. Close the publication and exit the software.

Text of *Antiques* file

Company

The Fairlawn Antiques Association is once again holding fairs around the country. Each year, the fair growds larger as more and more people take stalls and come along to find a bargain. Previously, the fairs concentrated on small items such as needlework tools, stamp boxes, lamps and ink-stands, but this year we have seven organizations offering visitors the chance to buy a sofa, daybed, sideboard or chair. Make sure, therefore, that you have a large van or take advantage of our Van Hire offer. Details available at the entrance.

Venues

There are seven fairs being held around the country this year – two more than last year. The towns we will be appearing at are: Oxford (September), Leicester (November), Cardiff (December), Newcastle (February), Bristol (April), Reading (June) and Cheltenham (July).

Each fair opens at 10.00 am and finishes at 4.00 pm. Stall-holders should arrive at 8.30 am. As always, Glenys and her team of willing helpers will be providing refreshments in the form of tea, coffee, home-made cakes and light lunches.

Television

In April, the Bristol fair will horst the popular BBC programme Antiques Roadshow so turn up early on that day as we can expect several hundred people to attend.

4

Answer 19a

ANTIQUES FAIR

Company
The Fairlawn Antiques Association is once again holding fairs around the country. Each year, the fair grows larger as more and more people take stalls and come along to find a bargain. Previously, the fairs concentrated on small items such as needlework tools, stamp boxes, lamps and inkstands, but this year we have seven organizations offering visitors the chance to buy a sofa, daybed, sideboard or chair. Make sure, therefore, that you have a large van or take advantage of our Van Hire offer. Details available at the entrance.

Venues
There are seven fairs being held around the country this year – two more than last year. The towns we will be appearing at are: Oxford (September), Leicester (November), Cardiff (December), Newcastle (February), Bristol (April), Reading (June) and Cheltenham (July). Each fair opens at 10.00 am and finishes at 4.00 pm. Stallholders should arrive at 8.30 am. As always, Glenys and her

team of willing helpers will be providing refreshments in the form of tea, coffee, home-made cakes and light lunches.

Television
In April, the Bristol fair will host the popular BBC programme *Antiques Roadshow* so turn up early on that day as we can expect several hundred people to attend.

My Name

Answer 19b

ANTIQUES FAIR

Company
The Fairlawn Antiques Association is once again holding fairs around the country. Each year, the fair grows larger as more and more people take stalls and come along to find a bargain.

Previously, the fairs concentrated on small items such as needlework tools, stamp boxes, lamps and inkstands, but this year we have seven organizations offering visitors the chance to buy a sofa, daybed, sideboard or chair. Make sure, therefore, that you have a large van or take advantage of our Van Hire offer. Details available at the entrance.

Venues
There are seven fairs being held around the country this year — two more than last year. The towns we will be appearing at

are: Oxford (September), Leicester (November), Cardiff (December), Newcastle (February), Bristol (April), Reading (June) and Cheltenham (July). Each fair opens at 10.00

a m and finishes at 4.00 pm. Stallholders should arrive at 8.30 am. As always, Glenys and her team of willing helpers will be providing refreshments in the form of tea, coffee, home-made cakes and light lunches.

Roadshow
In April, the Bristol fair will host the popular BBC programme Antiques Roadshow so turn up early on that day as we can expect several hundred people to attend.

My Name

Exercise 20

Task 1

1. Create a new single-page publication.

2. Set up the master page/template as follows:

    a) A4 paper size.

    b) Landscape orientation.

    c) Left, right, top and bottom margins 3 cm.

3. Add the date in the top margin.

4. Save this publication as *Puppets1*.

5. Set up the layout in a newsletter format, to include a page-wide heading above two columns of text.

    a) Column widths equal.

    b) Space between 1 cm.

6. Enter a heading THINGS TO MAKE at the top of the page in a serif font.

7. Increase the size of the heading text so that it extends across the full width of both columns of text.

Task 2

8. Import the text file *Puppets* so that it begins at the top of the left-hand column, below the heading.

9. Format the body text to be left aligned, in a sans serif font.

10. Check and correct the two spelling mistakes.

11. Import the image *Puppet* and place it within the first column, at the bottom of the page, making sure it does not cover any text.

12. Make sure your publication fits onto one page.

13. Save the publication with the same name and print a composite proof copy.

Task 3

14. Now draw a thick line below the heading to separate it from the two columns. Make sure it does not overlap any text.

15. Make the image smaller and flip it horizontally.

16. Move it to the top of the second column. Make sure it does not extend into the margin.

17. Apply a serif font to the subheadings.

18. Save as *Puppets2*.

Task 4

19. Increase the size of the subheadings: Rainy Days, Paper Plate Puppets, Finger Puppets and Sock Puppets so that they are larger than the body text but smaller than the heading text.

20. Change the body text to fully justified.

21. Reword the first subheading to read: Rainy Day Fun.

22. Format the body text so that there is space after each paragraph.

23. Adjust the size of the text so that the columns are balanced at the bottom of the page. Make sure the heading, subheadings and body text are still different sizes.

24. Make sure your printed publication fits onto one page. Save with the same name and print a copy of the publication, ensuring it fits on one page.

25. Close the publication and exit the software.

Text of *Puppets* file

Rainy Days

When the chilren are bored and cannot go out into the garden to play, why not make things? Here are three different types of puppet that are easy and enjoyable to make and will also be toys they can use to put on plays or for other games.

Paper Plate Puppets

You will need paper plates, a stapler or sticky tape, scraps of wool and card, non-toxic glue and paints, felt pens or crayons. Tape two plates together, leaving a gap big enough for your hand. Keeping the gap at the bottom, paint a face and use woool or paper for extra decoration e.g. hair, earrings etc. Put your hand through the gap and make your puppet talk and move around.

Finger Puppets

For these, you will need strips of paper or thin card about 8 cm wide and as tall as your tallest finger. Roll a strip into a tube to fit over your finger, and fasten with tape or glue. Give your puppet armds with scraps of paper, then paint or stick on faces. If you like, make one for every finger.

Sock Puppets

Find an old sock and put your fingers in the toe and thumb in the heel. Stick on googly eyes and material ears and you can move your fingers to make it 'talk'.

Answer 20a

12/6/06

THINGS TO MAKE

Rainy Days
When the children are bored and cannot go out into the garden to play, why not make things? Here are three different types of puppet that are easy and enjoyable to make and will also be toys they can use to put on plays or for other games.

Paper Plate Puppets
You will need paper plates, a stapler or sticky tape, scraps of wool and card, non-toxic glue and paints, felt pens or crayons. Tape two plates together, leaving a gap big enough for your hand. Keeping the gap at the bottom, paint a face and use wool or paper for extra decoration e.g. hair, earrings etc. Put your hand through the gap and make your puppet talk and move around.

Finger Puppets
For these, you will need strips of paper or thin card about 8cm wide and as tall as your tallest finger. Roll a strip into a tube to fit over your finger, and fasten with tape or glue. Give your puppet arms with scraps of paper, then paint or stick on faces. If you like, make one for every finger.

Sock Puppets
Find an old sock and put your fingers in the toe and thumb in the heel. Stick on googly eyes and material ears and you can move your fingers to make it 'talk'.

4

Answer 20b

12/6/06

THINGS TO MAKE

Rainy Day Fun
When the children are bored and cannot go out into the garden to play, why not make things? Here are three different types of puppet that are easy and enjoyable to make and will also be toys they can use to put on plays or for other games.

Paper Plate Puppets
You will need paper plates, a stapler or sticky tape, scraps of wool and card, non-toxic glue and paints, felt pens or crayons. Tape two plates together, leaving a gap big enough for your hand. Keeping the gap at the bottom, paint a face and use wool or paper for extra decoration e.g. hair, earrings etc. Put your hand through the gap and make your puppet talk and move around.

Finger Puppets
For these, you will need strips of paper or thin card about 8cm wide and as tall as your tallest finger. Roll a strip into a tube to fit over your finger, and fasten with tape or glue. Give your puppet arms with scraps of paper, then paint or stick on faces. If you like, make one for every finger.

Sock Puppets
Find an old sock and put your fingers in the toe and thumb in the heel. Stick on googly eyes and material ears and you can move your fingers to make it 'talk'.

UNIT 5

Creating an e-presentation

For this unit, you must be able to create a 3-slide presentation displaying images and different levels of text, and then print the slides, an outline of the text or audience handouts displaying a thumbnail picture of each slide.

EXERCISES 1, 2 AND 3

Test your ability to:

♦ Use appropriate software

♦ Create a new presentation

♦ Enter text

♦ Create text frames

♦ Save a presentation

♦ Close a presentation

Assessment Objectives: 1a, 1b, 2a, 2c, 4a and 4c

Exercise 1
1. Open your software.

2. You want a slide with one title frame and one main frame. Either create these or apply a suitable slide layout.

3. Enter the title: Fireworks Display.

4. In the main frame, enter the following text on two lines: Riverbank Hotel Henley-on-Thames.

5. Create a third frame below the main frame and enter the text: Saturday, 24th July 8–10 p.m.

6. Save the presentation as *Fireworks* and close the file.

Answer

> # Fireworks Display
>
> ## Riverbank Hotel
> ## Henley-on-Thames
>
> Saturday, 24ᵗʰ July 8 – 10 pm

Exercise 2
1. Start a new presentation.
2. You want a slide layout with a title frame and main frame.
3. Enter the title: Caring for Cats.
4. Enter the main text on 2 lines: A talk by Dr. Hamish McBean.
5. Save the presentation as *Cats*.
6. Close the file.

Answer

> # Caring for Cats
>
> ## A talk by
> ## Dr. Hamish McBean

Exercise 3 1. Start a new presentation and select a slide with a title frame and main frame.

2. Add the title: Books for Boys.

3. Add the following main text: A talk on the best buys for Christmas.

4. Create a new frame, positioned underneath the main frame, and enter the text: Presented by famous author Ian James.

5. Save as *Books* and then close the presentation.

Answer

EXERCISES 4, 5 AND 6

Test your ability to:

▶ Apply a background

▶ Insert a graphic/image

Assessment Objectives: 1c and 3a

Exercise 4 1. Start a new presentation.

2. Create a title frame and enter the text: Travelling to Madeira.

3. Add the following text in a new frame below the title: Sandie Drayton.

4. Format the slide background to pale orange.

5. Import the image *Beach* and place it in the top left-hand corner of the slide. Make sure it does not overlap any text.

6. Save the presentation as *Madeira* and close the file.

Answer

Exercise 5 1. Start a new presentation.

2. Create a title frame and enter the title: Dutch Bulbs.

3. Format the background to yellow.

4. Insert the image *Tulip* and position it centrally below the title. Make sure it does not overlap any text.

5. Create a new text frame and position this in the top right-hand corner of the slide. Enter the text: Gardensense Nurseries.

6. Save your presentation as *Bulbs*.

7. Close the file.

Answer

Exercise 6   1.   Start a new presentation.

2. Enter the following text as a main heading: **Farming Today**.

3. Insert the image *Lamb* and position it under the heading.

4. Create a new text frame and enter the text: **Save Our Countryside**. Position this text in the top left-hand corner of the slide.

5. Apply a green background to the slide.

6. Save the presentation as *Farming* and then close the file.

Answer

EXERCISES 7, 8 AND 9

Test your ability to:

- Open a previously saved presentation
- Use specified font sizes
- Add or remove bullets
- Align text
- Apply enhancement
- Save with a new name

Assessment Objectives: 2e, 2f, 2g and 2h

Exercise 7   1.   Open the presentation *Fireworks*.

2.   Apply a yellow background.

3.   Insert the image *Fireworks* and position it above the title.

4.   Format the title to bold, font size 50.

5.   Format the text Riverbank Hotel, Henley-on-Thames to italic, font size 32.

6.   Amend the details of date and time so that they form a bulleted list of two items.

7.   Add a third list item: Refreshments available.

8.   Save with the new name *Display* and then close the file.

Answer

Exercise 8   1.   Start a new presentation that has one title frame and one main frame.

2.   Enter the title LIBRARIES.

3.   Enter the heading The main libraries of Oxfordshire in the main frame and then add the following four items below the heading as a bulleted list: Witney, Oxford, Banbury and Henley.

4.   Format the title to a different font, e.g. Broadway, size 48.

5.   Format the main text to the same font, but size 30.

6.   Save the file as *Library books*.

7.   Underline the heading and format the list items to italic.

8.   Insert the image *Library* and position it in the top left-hand corner, making sure it does not obscure any text.

9. Apply a coloured background to the presentation.

10. Save the presentation as *Libraries* and then close the file.

Answer

Exercise 9 1. Open *Farming*.

2. Apply a bold format to the heading and increase the font size to 48.

3. Move the image to the top right-hand corner, and resize it so that it does not interfere with any text.

4. Create a new text frame and enter the following as a bulleted list:

   Corn
   Poultry
   Sheep
   Maize
   Exotic Fruits

5. Left-align the list, set a font size of 28 and format to italic.

6. Save with a new file name *Foods* and then close the file.

5

Answer

Save Our Countryside

Farming Today

- *Corn*
- *Poultry*
- *Sheep*
- *Maize*
- *Exotic Fruits*

EXERCISES 10, 11 AND 12

Test your ability to:

▶ Insert new slides

▶ Work with the slide master

▶ Set headers and footers

▶ Print slides

Assessment Objectives: 2a, 4e and 4f

Exercise 10 1. Reopen the presentation *Cats* and insert a second slide.

2. Create a title frame and main frame.

3. Enter the title: Contents.

4. In the main frame, add the following four points as a bulleted list: Types of Cat, Food, Illness and Breeding.

5. Insert the image *Cat* and position this on the left of the list, making sure it does not overlap any text.

6. Create a third frame and position this centrally below the list. Enter the text Video available, right aligned.

7. On the master slide, format the title text to bold size 40 and the main text to italic size 30.

8. Apply a pale green background to the entire presentation.

9. Add slide numbers.

10. Save these changes and print a copy of each slide, one per page.

11. Close the presentation.

Answer (Slide 2)

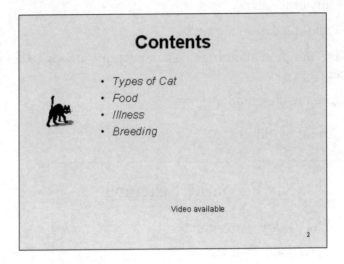

Exercise 11 1. Create a 3-slide presentation.

2. On Slide 1, enter the title: Radio Programmes.

3. On Slide 2, enter the title: BBC Output.

4. Below this, add the following text as a bulleted list, centre aligned: Radio 1, Radio 2, Radio 3 and Radio 4.

5. On Slide 3, enter the title: My Favourite Listening.

6. Add the following 5 items as a non-bulleted list:

The Today Programme
Afternoon Theatre
The Archers
The News Quiz
Question Time

7. On the master slide, make the following amendments:

   a) Format the title text to a different font, e.g. Times New Roman, size 48 underlined, and the main text to the same font, size 40 italic.

   b) Insert the image *Radio* and position it in the bottom right-hand corner. Make sure it will not interfere with text on any slides.

   c) Apply a pale background colour or leave it white.

   d) Create a new text frame and add your name in font size 14. Centre this frame under the main frame and ensure it does not interfere with any other text.

   e) Add the date as a footer.

8. Save the presentation as *Radio* and print a copy of all the slides, one per page.

9. Close the presentation.

Answer   Printout of slide 3

My Favourite Listening

The Today Programme

Afternoon Theatre

The Archers

The News Quiz

Question Time

My name

01 July 2005

Exercise 12

1. Open the file *Bulbs*.

2. Insert a new slide and enter the heading: Climbers.

3. Add the following main text: There are numerous plants you can use to cover walls and fences. Why not try Honeysuckle, Clematis, Rose or Jasmine?

4. Insert the image *Jasmine* and position it in the bottom left-hand corner of the slide.

5. Right-align the main text.

6. Go to Master Slide view and make these amendments:

a) Apply a different font to the heading and main text.

b) Format the heading to bold and underlined.

c) Add a new text frame and enter your name. Format the text to italic, font size 14. Position this frame in the bottom right-hand corner and ensure it does not obscure any text.

7. Return to Slide 2 and apply a pink background colour.

8. Print the slides, one to a page.

9. Save the changes and close the file.

Answer

EXERCISES 13, 14 AND 15

Test your ability to:

◗ Change slide order

◗ Delete text

◗ Promote and demote text

◗ Insert drawn objects

◗ Shade or fill drawn objects

◗ Set page or slide orientation

Assessment Objectives: 2b, 2i, 2k, 3b, 3c and 4d

Exercise 13

1. Create a new 3-slide presentation.

2. On Slide 1, enter the text Shopping on the Internet.

3. On Slide 2, enter the title What to buy.

4. Under this, type the following as a 7-item bulleted list: Groceries, Appliances, Washing machine, Cooker, Holidays, UK, Abroad.

5. On Slide 3, enter the title Security. Add the following as a 2-item list without any bullets: Padlock, Web address begins https.

6. Save as *Web* and print a copy of all the slides, one per page.

7. Apply a cream background to the presentation.

8. Using the master, format the text as follows:

   a) title text – bold, centred, font size 45

   b) Main text, level 1 – italic, font size 35, left aligned

   c) Main text, level 2 – no emphasis, font size 30, indented.

9. Make sure the following are visible on all slides:

   a) Add the image *Shop* and place it in the top left-hand corner.

   b) Add a text frame in the bottom right-hand corner and enter the text: Safe and Secure.

   c) Draw an oval shape and position this on the right of the slide. Shade it green.

10. On Slide 2, demote the text Washing machine, Cooker, UK and Abroad to level 2.

11. Delete the word Groceries and do not leave a bullet.

12. Re-order the slides so that *Security* becomes Slide 2.

13. Change the slides to portrait orientation.

14. Save as *Shopping* and print a copy of all the slides.

15. Close the file.

Answer   13a

Shopping on the Internet

1

What to buy
- Groceries
- Appliances
- Washing machine
- Cooker
- Holidays
- UK
- Abroad

2

Security

Padlock
Web address begins https

3

Answer   13b

1

2

3

Exercise 14 **1.** Create a new 2-slide presentation.

2. On the first slide, enter the title Beckingham School of Art.

3. Below this add the text in a new frame: Serving the Community.

4. On Slide 2, enter the title Courses for Next Year.

5. Add the following in a new frame as a bulleted list, centre aligned and at the level shown in brackets:

Fine Art (L1)
Painting (L1)
Drawing (L1)
Photography (L2)
Crafts (L2)
Silversmith (L1)
Pottery (L1)
Weaving (L2)

6. On the master slide, insert the image *Art* and position it in the top right-hand corner.

7. Reformat the text as follows:

a) Title text font size 48, bold and left aligned

b) Level 1 text font size 40, italic, centred, bulleted

c) Level 2 text no emphasis, size 30, centred, bulleted.

8. Apply a green background to the presentation.

9. Save as *Courses* and print a copy of both the slides.

10. Now make the following amendments:

a) Demote the text **Painting, Drawing** and **Pottery** to level 2.

b) Promote the text **Photography** and **Crafts** to level 1.

c) Delete the line **Silversmith**.

d) Change the title on Slide 2 to read **Courses Next Year**.

11. Add an upward-pointing arrow on the left of both slides, making sure it does not obscure any text. Border the arrow with a thick black line and fill with a contrasting colour to the background.

12. Save the presentation with the file name *Courses 2* and print a copy of the amended slides before closing.

Answer 14a

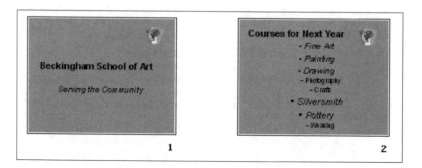

Answer 14b

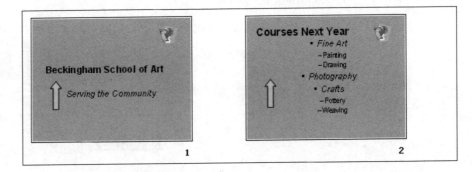

Exercise 15
1. Open *Bulbs*.

2. Insert a third slide.

3. Add the heading **Vegetables** and right-align.

4. Add the following text in a new frame as a non-bulleted list, centre aligned and at the level shown in brackets:

   Root Vegetables (L1)
   Carrots (L1)
   Potatoes (L1)
   Parsnips (L2)
   Salads (L2)
   Cucumber (L1)
   Tomatoes (L1)
   Peppers (L2)

5. Save these changes and print a copy of all the slides.

6. Apply a dark green background colour to the third slide.

7. Now make the following amendments:

   a) Demote the text **Carrots**, **Potatoes**, **Cucumber** and **Tomatoes** to level 2.

   b) Promote the text **Salads** to level 1.

   c) Delete the line **Potatoes**, leaving no gaps.

   d) Left-align the list.

8. On this slide only, draw a thick vertical line down the centre and colour it white.

9. Change the title on Slide 2 to read **Colourful Climbers**.

10. Re-order the presentation so that **Vegetables** becomes Slide 2 and **Colourful Climbers** is now Slide 3.

11. Save the presentation with the new file name *Vegetables* and print a copy of the amended slides.

12. Finally print a copy of Slide 3 only, in portrait orientation.

13. Close the presentation.

Answer 15a – Slide 3

Answer 15b – Re-ordered

1 2 3

Answer 15c – Slide 3 portrait

EXERCISES 16 AND 17

Test your ability to:

▶ Use the spell checker

▶ Replace specified text

▶ Print handouts

▶ Print an outline of the presentation

Assessment Objectives: 2d, 2j, 4g and 4h

Exercise 16 1. Create a 3-slide presentation.

2. On Slide 1 enter the title Cooking for Boys.

3. In a new frame, enter the text Helen Long Chef.

4. Create a third frame and position this centrally at the bottom of the slide. Enter the text Holingdale School.

5. On Slide 2, enter the title **Programme**. Under this, add the following as a bulleted list:

    Breakfast
    Packed Lunch
    Supper Dishes
    Boys Who Cook

6. On Slide 3 enter the title **Boys Who Cook** and then add the following as a bulleted list, at the level shown in brackets:

    Favourite Puddings (1)
    Fresh Fruit (1)
    Meat Dishes (2)
    Lamb (1)
    Beef (1)
    Pork (2)
    Healthy Boys (2)
    Vegetarians (1)

7. On the master slide, set the text styles as follows:

    a) Title – bold, size 46, centred

    b) Level 1 – italic, size 36, left aligned

    c) Level 2 – underlined, size 30 indented.

    d) Insert the image *Cooking* and position it at the top left of the slide, making sure it does not obscure any text.

    e) Apply a coloured background of your choice or leave as white.

8. Use the spell check facility to check the accuracy of the text.

9. Save the presentation as *Cooking* and print one copy of each slide.

10. Now make the following amendments:

    a) Replace the word **Boys** with **Kids** wherever it appears (4 times).

    b) Demote **Fresh Fruit** and **Lamb** to level 2.

    c) Delete the line **Beef**.

    d) Promote **Meat Dishes** and **Healthy Kids** to level 1.

11. Save these changes.

12. Print a handout showing all 3 slides as thumbnails on one page.

13. You need an outline: add the date as a header and then print an outline of the text of your presentation.

14. Close the presentation.

Answer   16a

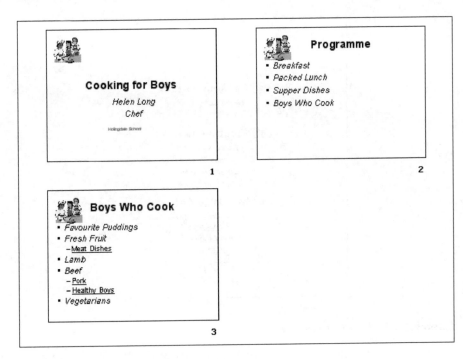

Answer   16b

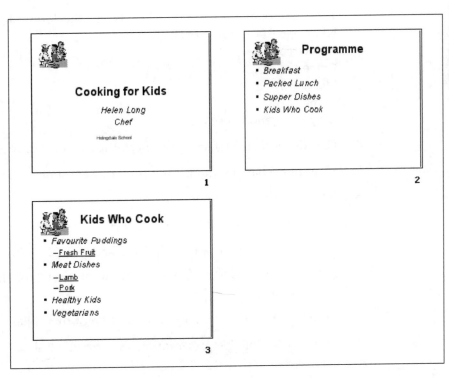

12/8/06

1 ▣ **Cooking for Kids**
    Helen Long
    Chef

2 ▣ **Programme**
    • *Breakfast*
    • *Packed Lunch*
    • *Supper Dishes*
    • *Kids Who Cook*

3 ▣ **Kids Who Cook**
    • *Favourite Puddings*
      – <u>*Fresh Fruit*</u>
    • *Meat Dishes*
      – <u>*Lamb*</u>
      – <u>*Pork*</u>
    • *Healthy Kids*
    • *Vegetarians*

Exercise 17

1. Re-open *Radio*.

2. Replace the word **Radio** with **BBC** wherever it appears (5 times).

3. Insert a new slide and enter the title **Television Viewing**.

   Type the following as a bulleted list, at the levels shown in brackets:
   News and Current Affairs (1)
   Panorama (1)
   Crime (2)
   Morse (2)
   Comedy (2)
   Only Fools and Horses (1)

4. Use the spell check facility to check the accuracy of the text.

5. Save these changes and print a copy of each slide on a separate page.

6. Now make the following amendments:

   a) Promote **Crime** and **Comedy** to level 1.

   b) Demote **Panorama** and **Only Fools and Horses** to level 2.

   c) Insert the line **Newsnight** into the list at level 2, below **Panorama** and above **Crime**.

   d) Delete the word **Viewing** from the title of this slide.

7. Print a copy of the presentation as a handout showing Slides 2–4 on one page.

8. You need an outline: add your name as a header and then print an outline of the text of your presentation.

9. Save the changes and close the file.

Answer 17a

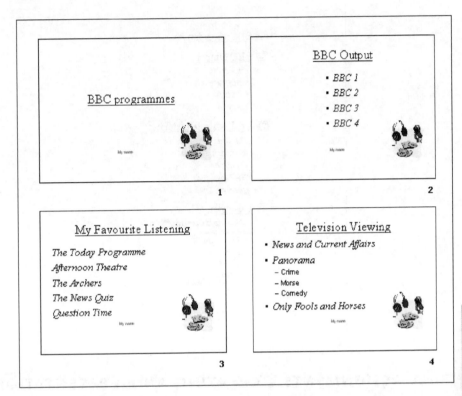

Answer 17b – Slide 4

My Name

1. BBC programmes
2. BBC Output
   - *BBC 1*
   - *BBC 2*
   - *BBC 3*
   - *BBC 4*
3. My Favourite Listening
   The Today Programme
   Afternoon Theatre
   The Archers
   The News Quiz
   Question Time
4. Television
   - *News and Current Affairs*
     – Panorama
     – Newsnight
   - *Crime*
     – Morse
   - *Comedy*
     – Only Fools and Horses

FULL ASSIGNMENTS – CREATING AN E-PRESENTATION

Exercise 18   You are going to prepare a presentation for a talk on applying for jobs.

Task 1

1. Create or amend the master slide as follows:

   a) Set slide orientation to landscape.

   b) Create a page-wide title frame at the top of the page.

   c) Create a page-wide main frame below the title frame.

   d) Set up the text styles as follows:

       i) Title frame – bold, size 50, no bullets, right aligned

       ii) Main frame level 1 – italic, size 36, left aligned, bullets

       iii) Main frame level 2 – underlined, size 28, bulleted, centred.

   e) Enter your name as a footer.

f) Format the background to white.

g) Display the slide number on the bottom right of the slide.

2. Save the master slide as *Vacancies* and use it to create a 3-slide presentation.

Task 2

3. On Slide 1, enter the title Filling that Vacancy but leave the main frame blank.

4. Insert the image *Interview* at the bottom right-hand corner of the slide.

5. On Slide 2, enter the title The Vacancy Process. Enter the following text as a list in the main frame at level 1:

Finding that Vacancy
Letters of Application
Curriculum Vitae
Interviews
Questions

6. On Slide 3 enter the title Your Winning CV. Enter the following text in the main frame as a list at the levels shown in brackets:

Personal Details (1)
Skills (2)
Employment (1)
Leisure (1)
Qualifications (2)
Exam Results (2)
Courses (1)

7. Use the spell check facilities to check for errors.

8. Update the file to save the changes, keeping the same file name.

9. Print a copy of each slide, one to a page, maintaining landscape orientation.

Task 3

10. Now make the following changes:

a) On Slide 3, delete the line Employment.

b) Add the line Voluntary or paid work at level 2 on the same slide, between Leisure and Qualifications.

c) Demote the lines Courses and Leisure to level 2.

d) Promote the lines Qualifications and Skills to level 1.

e) Replace the word Vacancy with Job wherever it appears (three times), maintaining capitals where necessary.

11. Create Slide 4 and enter the heading Interviews.

12. Create a rectangle that fills the main area of the slide.

13. Fill it with a dark colour.

14. Save the amended presentation as *Jobs*.

15. Print Slides 2–4 as a handout, with three slides on one page.

Task 4

16. Re-order the slides so that Slide 3 becomes Slide 4.

17. Create an outline of the presentation. Add your name as a header or footer on the page and print the presentation in outline view.

18. Close the presentation and exit the software.

Answer 18a

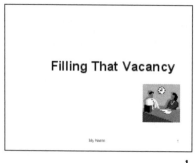

Answer 18b

Answer 18c

Exercise 19

Task 1

You are going to produce a presentation on holding a celebration.

1. Set the page to portrait orientation.

2. Create or amend the master slide as follows:

    a) Create a page-wide title frame at the top of the page.

    b) Create a page-wide main frame below the title frame.

    c) Set up the text styles as follows:

    i) Title frame – bold, size 48 no bullets, centred

    ii) Main frame level 1 – no emphasis, size 32, left aligned, bullets

    iii) Main frame level 2 – italic, size 24, bulleted, left, indented.

    d) Add your name and today's date as a footer.

    e) Add the slide number.

    f) Format the background to pink.

3. Save the master slide as *Celebration* and use it to create a 3-slide presentation.

Task 2

4. On Slide 1, enter the title **Celebration Plan**.

5. Place the image *Party* in the bottom left-hand corner of the slide, making sure it does not overlap any text.

6. On Slide 2, enter the title **A Successful Celebration**. Add the following text in the main frame as a list, all at level 1:

    Great Food
    Themes
    Celebration Games
    The Right Mix
    Take away Gifts

7. On Slide 3, enter the title **Games To Play** and the following text as a list in the main frame, at the levels shown in brackets:

    Active (1)
    Tag (1)
    Sardines (2)
    Simon Says (2)
    Verbal (2)
    Going Shopping (2)
    Singing (1)

8. Check and correct any errors.

9. Save the changes to update the presentation.

10. Print a copy of each slide, one to a page, in portrait orientation.

Task 3

11. Add the following line to Slide 3, after **Going Shopping** and before **Singing**: Alphabet (level 2).

12. On Slide 3, demote the lines **Tag** and **Singing** to level 2 and promote the line **Verbal** to level 1.

13. Replace the word **Celebration** with **Party** wherever it appears (3 times).

14. Add a new Slide 4 with the title **Help to Clear Up**.

15. On this slide, draw a star shape, border it with a thick line and fill with a dark colour.

16. Now delete the line **The Right Mix** on Slide 2 without leaving a gap.

17. Save the amended slideshow as *Party*.

18. Print a handout showing Slides 2–4 with all the slides on 1 page.

Task 4

19. Move Slide 4 so that it becomes Slide 2.

20. Print an outline of the text of the entire presentation on 1 page, first adding your name as a header or footer.

21. Save the file with the same name.

22. Close the presentation and exit the software.

Answer   19a

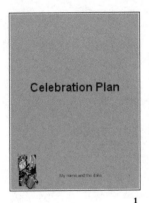

1   2   3

Answer 19b

Answer 19c

My Name

1 ▣ **Party Plan**

2 ▣ **Help to Clear Up**

3 ▣ **A Successful Party**
- Great Food
- Themes
- Party Games
- Take-away Gifts

4 ▣ **Games To Play**
- Active
  - *Tag*
  - *Sardines*
  - *Simon Says*
- Verbal
  - *Going Shopping*
  - *Alphabet*
  - *Singing*

Exercise 20

Task 1

You are going to prepare a slide show for the villa holiday company *Away From It All.*

1. Create or amend the master slide as follows:

   a) Set the slide orientation to landscape.

   b) Create a page-wide title frame at the top of the page.

   c) Create a page-wide main frame below the title frame.

   d) Set up the text styles as follows:

      i) Title frame – underlined, size 44, no bullets, right aligned

      ii) Main frame level 1 – bold, size 36, left aligned, bullets

      iii) Main frame level 2 – italic, size 30, bulleted, indented.

   e) In the footer, enter the text: **Miles Fergus, Marketing Manager.**

   f) Format the background to white.

2. Save the master slide as *Away* and use it to create a 3-slide presentation.

Task 2

3. On Slide 1, enter the title **Away From It All.**

4. Place the image *Holiday* in the top left-hand corner of the slide, making sure it does not obscure any text.

5. On Slide 2, enter the title **Our Holidays** and then enter the following as a list in the main frame, all at level 1:

   Perfect Location
   House with Pool
   Good Value
   House Share
   Maid Service

6. On Slide 3, enter the title **House Locations** and then enter the following as a list in the main frame, at the levels shown in brackets:

   Cyprus (1)
   Paphos (2)
   Spain (2)
   Seville (1)
   France (2)
   Nice (2)
   Paris (1)

7. Use the spell check facility to correct any errors.

8. Save these changes, keeping the file name *Away*, and print a copy of each slide, one per page.

Task 3

9. Now make the following changes:.

   a) On Slide 3, add Cordoba (level 2) between Seville and France.

   b) On the same slide, demote Seville and Paris to level 2 and promote Spain and France to level 1.

   c) Replace the word House with Villa wherever it appears (3 times).

10. Create a new Slide 4 with the title Cheapest Prices.

11. Draw a smiley face or simple circle. Border with a thick, dark line and fill with a pale colour.

12. Save the amended presentation as *Villas*.

13. Print all 4 slides as a handout with 4 thumbnail slides per page.

Task 4

14. On Slide 2, delete the line Good Value.

15. Re-order the slides so that Slide 3 becomes Slide 4.

16. Create an outline of the presentation. Add your name as a header and print a copy on one page.

17. Save these changes to update the file, keeping the filename *Villas*.

18. Close the presentation and exit the software.

Answer 20a

Away From It All

1

Our Holidays
- Perfect Location
- House with Pool
- Good Value
- House Share
- Maid Service

Miss Fergus, Marketing Manager

2

House Locations
- **Cyprus**
  - *Paphos*
  - *Spain*
- **Seville**
  - *France*
  - *Nice*
- **Paris**

Miss Fergus, Marketing Manager

3

Answer 20b

Away From It All

Miss Fergus, Marketing Manager

Our Holidays
- Perfect Location
- Villa with Pool
- Good Value
- Villa Share
- Maid Service

Miss Fergus, Marketing Manager

Villa Locations
- **Cyprus**
  - *Paphos*
- **Spain**
  - *Seville*
  - *Cordoba*
- **France**
  - *Nice*
  - *Paris*

Miss Fergus, Marketing Manager

Cheapest Prices

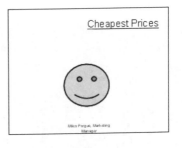

Miss Fergus, Marketing Manager

Answer 20c

My Name

1 ▣ <u>Away From It All</u>

2 ▣ <u>Our Holidays</u>
- Perfect Location
- Villa with Pool
- Villa Share
- Maid Service

3 ▣ <u>Cheapest Prices</u>

4 ▣ <u>Villa Locations</u>
- Cyprus
  - *Paphos*
- Spain
  - *Seville*
  - *Cordoba*
- France
  - *Nice*
  - *Paris*

UNIT **6**

E-image creation

Using appropriate software, you will need to demonstrate that you can create artwork of a set size that incorporates images, shapes and text and can print it out accurately in colour. You must also be able to download and make use of images from a digital camera.

EXERCISES 1, 2 AND 3

Test your ability to:

▸ Create a new document

▸ Import an image

▸ Position an image

▸ Crop an image

▸ Resize an image

▸ Save your work

Assessment Objectives: 1c, 1d, 1e, 1f and 4c

Exercise 1   1. Open your application and start a new document.

2. Insert the image *Windmill*.

3. Position the image in the top left-hand corner of the page.

4. Crop the image to remove the house.

5. Reduce the image to about half its original size, maintaining the proportions.

6. Save your document as *Windmill*.

Answer

Exercise 2 1. Start a new document.

2. Insert the image *Archery*.

3. Crop it to remove the target.

4. Increase it in size so that it is about 11 cm in height, maintaining the proportions.

5. Place the image in the centre of the page.

6. Save your document as *Archer*.

Answer

Exercise 3 1. Start a new document.

2. Insert the image *Wineglass*.

3. Crop it to remove the cork.

4. Amend its size so that it is about 7 cm in height, maintaining the proportions.

5. Place the image in the centre of the page.

6. Save your document as *Glass*.

Answer

EXERCISES 4, 5 AND 6

Test your ability to:

- ◗ Create artwork
- ◗ Set the size of a piece of artwork
- ◗ Insert an image into artwork
- ◗ Create a drawn shape
- ◗ Copy objects
- ◗ Resize shapes
- ◗ Print your artwork
- ◗ Close the file

Assessment Objectives: 1b, 1c, 1g, 3d, 3f, 4a and 4d

Exercise 4 1. Create a piece of artwork in the shape of a rectangle 8 cm high and 15 cm wide.

2. Insert a circle 1 cm in diameter.

3. Copy this shape three times to create four circles.

4. Position one circle in each corner of the artwork.

5. Insert the image *Compass* and centre it in the middle of the artwork.

6. Save your artwork as *Circles*.

7. Print one copy of the artwork.

8. Close the file.

Answer

Exercise 5   1. Create a new piece of artwork 15 cm wide and 10 cm high.

2. Insert a triangle that has a 2 cm wide base and position this in the centre of the artwork.

3. Make two copies of the triangle and position these on either side of the original shape. Join them with straight lines.

4. Double the size of the central triangle.

5. Save as *Triangles*.

6. Print a copy of the artwork and then close the file.

Answer

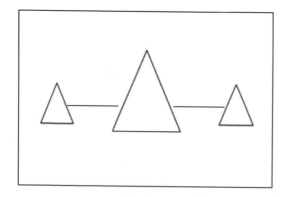

Exercise 6 1. Create a new piece of artwork 7 cm square.

2. Insert a rectangle that is 3 cm in height and 1 cm wide and position this in the top left-hand corner of the artwork.

3. Make two copies of the rectangle and position these side by side, underneath the original shape.

4. Halve the size of the top rectangle.

5. Insert the image *Seaside*.

6. Increase it in size so that it fills the right-hand half of the artwork.

7. Save as *Seaside shapes*.

8. Print a copy of the artwork and then close the file.

Answer

EXERCISES 7, 8 AND 9

Test your ability to:

▶ Rotate an object

▶ Delete an object

Assessment Objectives: 3b and 3g

Exercise 7 1. Create a new piece of artwork in the form of a circle 20 cm in diameter.

2. Insert a rectangle 5 cm wide and 8 cm high and position this on the left.

3. Insert the image *Watering* and resize it so that it is the same height as the rectangle. Place it on the right of the rectangle.

4. Now copy the rectangle, rotate the copy 90° and position it underneath the image.

5. Draw a vertical line between the original rectangle and the image, making sure it does not touch any object.

6. Save the file as *Watering* and print one copy.

7. Now delete the original rectangle.

8. Save the amended file as *Moved rectangle* and print a copy before closing.

Answer   7a

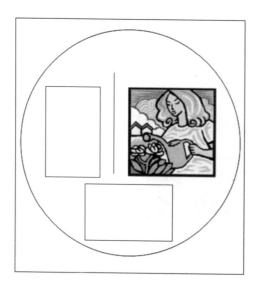

Answer   7b

Exercise 8 1. Create a new piece of artwork 10 cm wide and 6 cm high.

2. Draw an ellipse and place it centrally at the bottom of the artwork.

3. Import the image *Fencing*.

4. Crop it to remove one of the men.

5. Reduce the image in size and position it in the bottom right-hand corner of the artwork. Make sure it does not touch the ellipse.

6. Create a square 2 cm wide. Copy the square three times and position the four squares in a row inside the artwork across the top of the ellipse.

7. Save as *One man* and print a copy.

8. Now delete two of the squares.

9. Move the remaining two squares into the top left and right corners.

10. Rotate the ellipse so that it is now vertical, resizing if necessary to make sure it fits inside the artwork without touching the edges.

11. Save the file with the name *Ellipse* and print one copy before closing.

Answer   8a

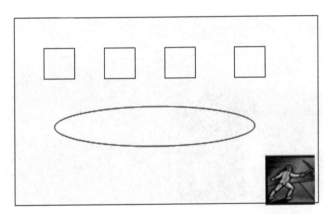

Answer   8b

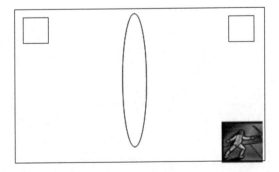

Exercise 9 1. Create a new piece of circular artwork that is 9 cm in diameter.

2. Draw a small square and place it centrally at the bottom of the artwork.

3. Import the image *Houses*.

4. Crop it to remove the house with the red roof.

5. Reduce the image in size if necessary and position it in the space above the square. Make sure it does not touch the sides of the artwork.

6. Create a triangle with a base about 2 cm wide. Copy it once and position the triangles on either side of the image.

7. Rotate the right-hand triangle 90° clockwise.

8. Save as *Pointing Triangle* and print a copy.

9. Now delete the square.

10. Move the right-hand triangle into the space it has left.

11. Rotate the left-hand triangle so that it is pointing in the opposite direction.

12. Reduce the size of the image and position it centrally in the artwork.

13. Save the file with the name *Two Triangles* and print one copy before closing.

Answer 9a

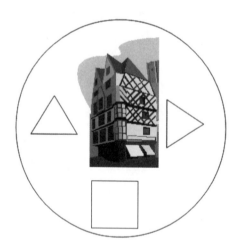

Answer 9b

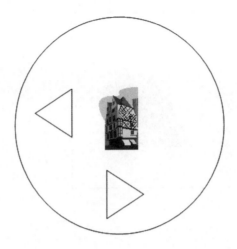

EXERCISES 10, 11 AND 12

Test your ability to:

▶ Use specified colours

▶ Flip items

Assessment Objectives: 3a and 3c

Exercise 10
1. Create a new piece of artwork 15 cm wide and 10 cm high.
2. Draw a large triangle and place this on the left.
3. Colour it yellow.
4. Copy the shape, colour it red and position it opposite the yellow triangle.
5. Insert the image *Roses* and crop it to remove the small heart.
6. Reduce it in size and position it inside the yellow triangle.
7. Save the artwork as *Roses* and print one copy in colour.
8. Flip the red triangle vertically so that it is upside down.
9. Delete the image inside the yellow triangle.
10. Save the amended artwork as *Red triangle* and print one copy in colour.
11. Close the file.

Answer 10a

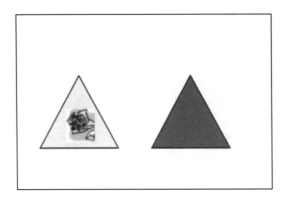

Answer 10b

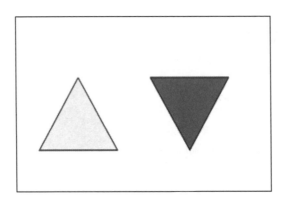

Exercise 11 1. Create a new piece of artwork 14 cm wide and 8 cm high.

2. Draw a line vertically down the centre.

3. In the top right-hand corner, insert a small square and colour it red.

4. Copy this shape three times and position the four squares in a block. Colour one green, one black and one white.

5. Insert the image *Cyclists* in the left-hand half of the artwork. Flip it horizontally to create a mirror image, so that the cyclists are facing in the opposite direction. If necessary, reduce the size slightly to make sure it does not extend outside the artwork or touch the vertical line.

6. Save the artwork as *Cyclists* and print one copy in colour.

7. Now delete the black square.

8. Move the red square to the bottom right-hand corner of the artwork.

9. Resize the image so that it is half its original size.

10. Rotate the line 90° so that it is horizontal, and position it centrally below the image and the two green and white squares.

11. Save the file as *New cycles* and print one copy in colour before closing.

Answer 11a

Answer 11b

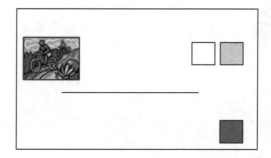

Exercise 12 **1.** Create a new piece of artwork 12 cm wide and 14 cm high.

2. Draw an oval 3 cm wide and place this on the left.

3. Copy the shape three times and line up the ovals down the left-hand side of the artwork.

4. Colour the top shape black, the second red, the third blue and the fourth yellow.

5. Insert the image *Pencils* and crop it to remove as much of the background as you can.

6. Reduce it in size and position it to the right of the black oval at the top of the artwork.

7. Save the artwork as *Pencil ovals* and print one copy in colour.

8. Flip the pencil image vertically so that it is upside down.

9. Delete the yellow oval.

10. Draw straight lines to join the pencil image to each of the remaining ovals.

11. Save the amended artwork as *Pencils and lines* and print one copy in colour.

12. Close the file.

Answer   12a

Answer 12b

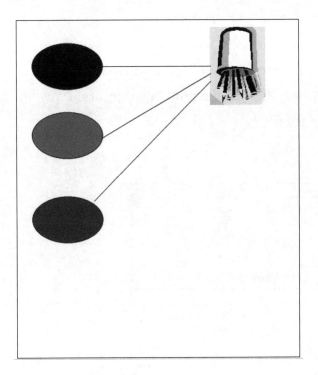

EXERCISES 13, 14 AND 15

Test your ability to:

▶ Add text

▶ Amend text

▶ Open artwork saved previously

Assessment Objectives: 2a and 2b

Exercise 13

1. Re-open *Circles*.

2. Draw four lines to join the circles.

3. Colour the circles blue.

4. Crop the image to remove the man.

5. Enter the text DRAWING CIRCLES IS FUN on one line and position this below the image, making sure it does not touch any lines or circles.

6. Save the file as *Coloured circles* and print one copy in colour.

7. Flip the image vertically.

8. Delete the two vertical lines.

9. Colour the circles so that they are now yellow.

10. Amend the text to read **DRAWING LINES IS FUN**.

11. Save these changes and print one copy of the artwork in colour.

12. Close the file.

Answer 13a

Answer 13b

Exercise 14 1. Re-open *New cycles*.

2. Insert a large triangle to the right of the image and enter the following text in black inside it, on three lines: **Go By Bike**.

3. Save the file as *Bike*.

4. Print one copy in colour.

5. Now change the text to read: **Go By Bicycle**.

6. Colour the text red.

7. Save these changes and print a final copy in colour before closing the file.

Answer 14a

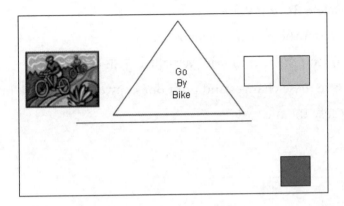

Answer 14b

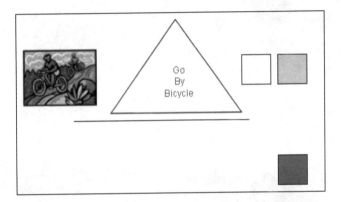

Exercise 15
1. Start a new piece of artwork and set the size as a square 6 cm by 6 cm.

2. Insert the image *Trophy*.

3. Crop the image to remove the people.

4. Reduce it in size to 3 cm high and position it in the centre of the artwork.

5. Draw any shape and then copy it four times.

6. Arrange the five shapes evenly round the image, reducing their size so that they fit inside the artwork without overlapping the edges. Make sure you leave a blank space underneath the image.

7. Colour the shapes orange.

8. Enter the text WINNING on one line and position this below the image, making sure it does not touch any objects.

9. Save the file as *Winning* and print one copy in colour.

10. Flip the image vertically.

11. Delete the top shape.

12. Colour the remaining shapes green.

13. Amend the text to read: WINNING THE CUP.

14. Save these changes and print one copy of the artwork in colour.

15. Close the file.

Answer 15a

Answer 15b

EXERCISES 16 AND 17

Test your ability to:

◆ Resize text to fit

Assessment Objective: 2a

Exercise 16 1. Create a new square piece of artwork. Set the size as 15 cm by 15 cm.

2. Enter the text SUMMER HOLIDAYS in black. Rotate the text anticlockwise 90° and move it to fit down the left-hand side of the artwork.

3. Size the text to fit the full height of the artwork.

4. Colour the background of the artwork yellow.

5. Insert a circle 5 cm in diameter on the right and colour it orange.

6. Create a small rectangle to represent a ray of the sun, colour it orange and position it vertically at the bottom of the circle. Copy this shape seven times and arrange the shapes evenly spaced out round the sun (as shown in the answer).

7. Save the file as *Sun* and print one copy in colour.

8. Now delete the lower three rectangles.

9. Insert the image *Beach* and resize it so that it fits below the circle.

10. Enter the text IN THE SUN inside the circle so that it is all on one line, and colour it red.

11. Save the file as *Holidays* and print one copy in colour.

12. Amend the text to read IN THE SUNSHINE and resize it so that it still fits on one line inside the circle.

13. Recolour the text in the circle black.

14. Save these changes and print a copy of the artwork in colour before closing the file.

Answer 16a

Answer 16b

Answer 16c – re-worded text

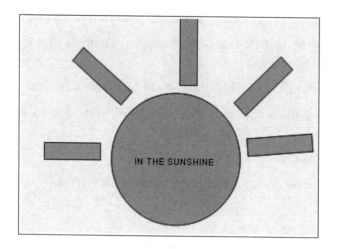

Exercise 17 **1.** Create a new piece of artwork in the form of a circle 15 cm in diameter.

2. Insert the image *Music*.

3. Flip it horizontally to create a mirror image and crop it to remove the triangles.

4. Position the image centrally inside the artwork.

5. Enter the text **NEW BAND** and colour it black.

6. Rotate the text 90° clockwise and position it down the right-hand side of the artwork. Size the text to fill the space.

7. Now enter the text **Josie Black** and position this above the image. Colour the text blue.

8. Create a square 2 cm wide and copy it twice. Position the three squares in a line below the image. Colour them all black.

9. Save the file as *Band* and print one copy in colour.

10. Now delete one square.

11. Re-colour one of the remaining squares blue.

12. Amend the vertical wording to read **NEW RECORDING** and resize the text to fit the space.

13. Draw a horizontal line below the squares but do not let it touch any objects.

14. Save the file with the new name *Revised Band* and print a copy in colour.

15. Close the file.

Answer 17a

Answer 17b

Test your ability to:

- Download a digital image from a camera
- Set artwork resolution
- Save a digital camera image
- Print in black and white

Assessment Objectives: 1a, 4b, 4c and 4d

Exercise 18

1. Using appropriate software, download any image from a digital camera.
2. On the image, add a word or phrase that describes what you can see.
3. Save the image with this word as the file name.
4. Print the image in black and white.
5. Open the image *bread.jpg*.
6. Change the resolution to 30 pixels/inch or 12 pixels/cm.
7. Save the amended image as *bread2.jpg*.
8. Print a copy of this image.
9. Close all files.

Answer 18a

Answer 18b – changing resolution

Exercise 19
1. Download a second image from a digital camera.
2. Add a suitable title and position this anywhere on the image.
3. Save the image with the title as its filename.
4. Print a copy in black and white.
5. Open the image *box.jpg*.
6. Change the resolution to 30 pixels/inch or 12 pixels/cm.
7. Save the amended image as *box2.jpg*.
8. Print a copy.
9. Close all files and applications.

Answer   19a – add text

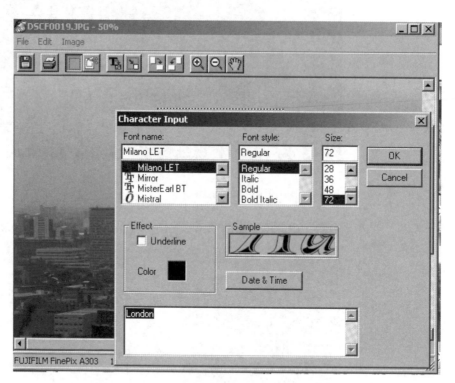

Answer   19b – printing in black and white

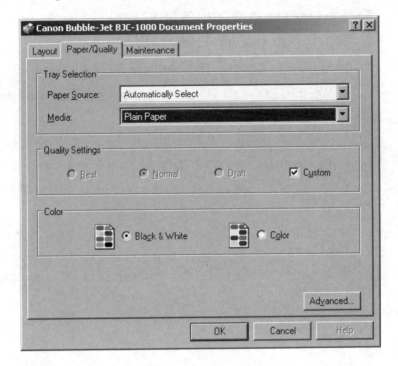

FULL ASSIGNMENTS – E-IMAGE CREATION

[You will need access to three digital camera images as well as the files on the CD.]

Exercise 20

Task 1

You are going to produce a draft design for a box of chocolates.

1. Create a new piece of artwork and set the size 9 cm wide and 10 cm high.

2. Fill the entire background pale blue.

3. Using the answer as a guide to the design, draw an ellipse and place it in a central position at the top of the artwork. Fill the ellipse white.

4. Import the image *Chocolate* and flip it horizontally.

5. Crop the image to remove the spoon.

6. Place the image in the centre of the ellipse, resizing it in proportion to fit the shape.

Task 2

7. Enter the text **CHOCOLATE BITES** in black.

a) Rotate the text 90° anticlockwise.

b) Move it to fit down the left-hand side of the artwork.

c) Size it to fit the height of the artwork but make sure it does not touch any objects or overlap the edge.

8. Draw a small circle and place this under the ellipse.

9. Copy the shape four times and place all five circles in a straight line.

10. Colour the 1st, 3rd and 5th circles dark blue and the 2nd and 4th circles white.

11. Import the image *Baking* and place it in the bottom right-hand corner of the artwork.

12. Enter the following text in brown: **Heaven to eat** and position it centrally under the circles.

13. Save the file as *Chocolates* and print one copy in colour.

Task 3

14. Now make the following amendments:

a) Delete the two white circles.

b) Amend the vertical text to **CHOCOBITES** and resize it so that it stretches to fit the full height of the artwork.

c) Change the colour of the text **Heaven to eat** to black.

15. Save the file as *New chocolates* and print one copy in colour.

16. Close the file.

Task 4

17. Using appropriate software, download any image from a digital camera.

18. On the image, add a word or phrase that describes what you can see.

19. Save the image with this word as the file name.

20. Print the image in black and white.

21. Open the image *tray.jpg*.

22. Change the resolution to 30 pixels/inch or 12 pixels/cm.

23. Save the amended image as *tray2.jpg*.

24. Print a copy of this image.

25. Close all files and applications.

Answer 20a

Answer 20b

Exercise 21

Task 1

You are going to design a new bookmark.

1. Create a piece of artwork 5 cm wide and 16 cm high.

2. Fill the entire background pale green.

3. Insert the image *Books* and make the following changes:

   a) Crop it to remove the shelves.

   b) Resize it so that it is no taller than 3 cm.

   c) Move it to near the top of the artwork as shown in the answer.

4. Below the image, enter the following text on three lines: VISIT YOUR LIBRARY TODAY! Colour it black.

5. Draw a rectangle 6 cm high and 3 cm wide and position this below the text. Fill it with white.

Task 2

6. Enter the text START READING and colour it black.

   a) Rotate the text 90° clockwise.

   b) Move it into the rectangle.

   c) Resize it to fit the full height of the shape.

7. Create a small circle and copy it three times. Position two circles above the image and two below the rectangle.

8. Colour the top two circles red and the bottom two circles black.

9. Save the file as *Bookmark* and print one copy in colour.

Task 3

10. Now amend the vertical text to READING and resize it to fit the full height of the shape.

11. Delete the two red circles.

12. Draw a small rectangle 1 cm high and 3.5 cm wide and position this above the image. Colour it yellow.

13. Save the file as *Bookmark 2* and print one copy in colour.

14. Close the file.

Task 4

15. Using appropriate software, download any image from a digital camera.

16. On the image, add a word or phrase that describes what you can see.

17. Save the image with this word as the file name.

18. Print the image in black and white.

19. Open the image *london.jpg*.

20. Change the resolution to 30 pixels/inch or 12 pixels/cm.

21. Save the amended image as *london2.jpg*.

22. Print a copy of this image.

23. Close all files and applications.

Answer 21a   *Answer* 21b

Exercise 22

Task 1

You are going to design a book cover.

1. Create a square piece of artwork 12 cm × 12 cm.

2. Import the image *Island*.

a) Flip the image so that the tree is on the right.

b) Crop it to remove the fish.

c) Resize it so that it is no more than 4 cm high.

d) Position it in the centre of the artwork.

3. Import the image *Money* and resize it so that it is half its original size, still maintaining its proportions. Position it in the top left-hand corner.

4. Draw a circle 2.5 cm in diameter and position this on the left of the island image. Colour it blue.

Task 2

5. Enter the text Only £20 in black on two lines and position it inside the circle, ensuring it does not touch any edge and the blue fill colour is displayed.

6. Draw a small triangle. Copy it twice and position the triangles in a row underneath the *Island* image. Colour them all yellow.

7. Enter the text ROBERT L. STEVENSON in black and position it at the bottom of the artwork, stretching it to fill the full width.

8. Draw a thick black line across the top of the text.

9. Enter the text ADVENTURE in black.

a) Rotate it 90° clockwise.

b) Position it down the right-hand side of the artwork and stretch it to fill the space but do not allow it to touch the line.

10. Now enter the text Treasure Island and colour it black. Place it centrally above the island image, leaving a clear space all round.

11. Save as *Book cover* and print one copy in colour.

Task 3

12. Now make the following amendments:

a) Change the author's name to read ROBERT LOUIS STEVENSON and resize it so that it is no wider than before.

b) Change the colour of the book title Treasure Island text to red.

c) Delete two triangles. Move the remaining triangle and position it centrally above the title text at the top of the artwork.

13. Save the artwork with the new file name *Final book cover* and print one copy in colour.

14. Close the file.

Task 4

15. Using appropriate software, download any image from a digital camera.

16. On the image, add a word or phrase that describes what you can see.

17. Save the image with this word as the file name.

18. Print the image in black and white.

19. Open the image *scales.jpg*.

20. Change the resolution to 30 pixels/inch or 12 pixels/cm.

21. Save the amended image as *scales2.jpg*.

22. Print a copy of this image.

23. Close all files and applications.

Answer 22a

UNIT 7

Web page creation

This unit requires you to create web pages that incorporate images and formatted text and include links to external websites, e-mail systems and internal pages on your computer. You must also be able to display the source HTML code.

EXERCISES 1, 2 AND 3

Test your ability to:

◗ Create a new document

◗ Insert a text file

◗ Save a document

◗ Save files into a named folder

Assessment Objectives: 1a, 1b, 1c and 2b

Exercise 1 You are going to create some web pages for your music shop.

1. Create a new document.

2. Insert the text file: *Don't Fret*.

3. Save the document as *music shop.htm* into the same folder housing the text file.

4. Rename this folder *Music*.

Text of *Don't Fret* file

Don't Fret Guitars

The best instruments money can buy

If you are looking for a new guitar, visit our shop in Brighton for the latest, cheapest and best-looking models.

Exercise 2
1. Start a new document.
2. Insert the text file *Models*.
3. Save the document as *guitars.htm* into the *Music* folder.

Text of *Models* file

New Guitar Models

Fender

If you are looking for a distinctive model, why not try the new Highway? It has a satin lacquer finish, maple neck and chrome hardware.

Only £599

Epiphone

Still popular, the latest Cortez is still a cracking model and a Sunburst will set you back £975.

Exercise 3
1. Start a new document.
2. Insert the text file *Champagne*.
3. Save the file as *france.htm* into the same folder housing the text file.
4. Rename this folder *Wine*.

Text of *Champagne* file

Champagne

This region of France is not just known for its wines.

Churches

Three to visit: the Cathedral of Our Lady, Reims; the church at Giffaumont-Champaubert; and the Church of St. Michael and St. Paul, Montier en Der which was destroyed in 1940 but rebuilt after the war.

Lakes

The largest man-made lake in Europe can be found here. It is the Lac du Der and has 77 km of shoreline.

Test your ability to:

- Enter text
- Check accuracy of text
- Edit text
- Use different font sizes
- Emphasize text
- Align page items

Assessment Objectives: 2a, 2c, 2f, 2g and 2i

Exercise 4

1. On the *music shop* page, format the text Don't Fret Guitars as a Heading (large font size).

2. Format the text The best instruments money can buy as a Subheading (medium font size).

3. Format the rest of the text as Body Text (small font size, not bold).

4. Ensure that each line is separated by a clear line space.

5. Format the text Don't Fret Guitars as centre aligned on the page.

6. Enter the text Open 7 days a week a few lines below the end of the text.

7. Format this to Body Text, italic, centre aligned.

8. Check all text for accuracy.

9. Save these changes to update the file.

Answer

Don't Fret Guitars

The best instruments money can buy

If you are looking for a new guitar, visit our shop in Brighton for the latest, cheapest and best-looking models.

Open 7 days a week

Exercise 5
1. On the *guitars* page, format the text New Guitar Models as a Heading (large font size).

2. Format the text Fender and Epiphone as Subheadings (medium font size).

3. Format the rest of the text as Body Text (small font size, italic).

4. Ensure that each line is separated by a clear line space.

5. Format the text New Guitar Models as centre aligned on the page.

6. Enter the text We take credit cards a few lines below the end of the text.

7. Format this to Body Text, italic, underlined and centre aligned.

8. Check for accuracy.

9. Save these changes to the file.

Answer

New Guitar Models

Fender

If you are looking for a distinctive model, why not try the new Highway?

It has a satin lacquer finish, maple neck and chrome hardware.

Only £599

Epiphone

Still popular, the latest Cortez is still a cracking model and a Sunburst will set you back £975.

<u>*We take credit cards*</u>

Exercise 6
1. On the *france* page, format the word Champagne as a Heading (large font size).

2. Format the text Churches and Lakes as Subheadings (medium font size).

3. Format the rest of the text as Body Text (small font size).

4. Ensure that each line is separated by a clear line space.

5. Format the title as centre aligned on the page.

6. Enter the text The best time to visit is late Spring or early Autumn a few lines below the end of the text.

7. Format this to Body Text, underlined and centre aligned.

8. Check for accuracy.

9. Save these changes to the file.

Answer

Champagne

This region of France is not just known for its wines.

Churches

Three to visit: the Cathedral of Our Lady, Reims; the church at Giffaunont-Champaubert and the Church of St. Michael and St. Paul, Montier en Der which was destroyed in 1940 but rebuilt after the war.

Lakes

The largest man-made lake in Europe can be found here. It is the Lac du Der and has 77 km of shoreline.

<u>The best time to visit is late Spring or early Autumn</u>

EXERCISES 7, 8 AND 9

Test your ability to:

◗ Insert and place an image on a webpage

◗ Change background colour

◗ Control text flow

Assessment Objectives: 2d, 2e, 2h and 2i

Exercise 7

1. Open the page *music shop*.

2. Import the image *Instruments* and position it so that it is just below the heading.

3. Centre the image on the page.

4. Apply an orange background colour.

5. Save these changes.

Answer

Don't Fret Guitars

The best instruments money can buy

If you are looking for a new guitar, visit our shop in Brighton for the latest, cheapest and best-looking models.

Open 7 days a week

Exercise 8
1. Open the page *guitars*.

2. Import the image *Guitar* and position it so that it is on the right of the page, below the heading.

3. Apply a pale green background colour.

4. Save these changes.

Answer

New Guitar Models

Fender

If you are looking for a distinctive model, why not try the new Highway?

It has a satin lacquer finish, maple neck and chrome hardware.

Only £599

Epiphone

Still popular, the latest Cortez is still a cracking model and a Sunburst will set you back £975.

We take credit cards

Exercise 9
1. Open the page *france.htm*.

2. Import the image *wineglass* and position it so that it is just below the heading.

3. Centre the image on the page.

4. Apply your own choice of background colour.

5. Save these changes.

Answer

Champagne

This region of France is not just known for its wines.

Churches

Three to visit: the Cathedral of Our Lady, Reims; the church at Giffaumont-Champaubert; and the Church of St. Michael and St. Paul, Montier en Der which was destroyed in 1940 but rebuilt after the war.

Lakes

The largest man-made lake in Europe can be found here. It is the Lac du Der and has 77 km of shoreline.

The best time to visit is late Spring or early Autumn

EXERCISES 10, 11 AND 12

Test your ability to:

◆ Link pages

◆ Insert an external link

◆ Test links

Assessment Objectives: 3a, 3b and 3c

Exercise 10 1. To link the *music shop* page to the *guitars* page, link the text new guitar on *music shop.htm* to *guitars.htm*.

2. Save the amended page.

3. Now create an external link on *guitars.htm* to the Fender website at www.fender.com. Use the subheading *Fender* as the link text.

4. Save the amended page.

5. Load the pages into a browser and test both links.

Answer

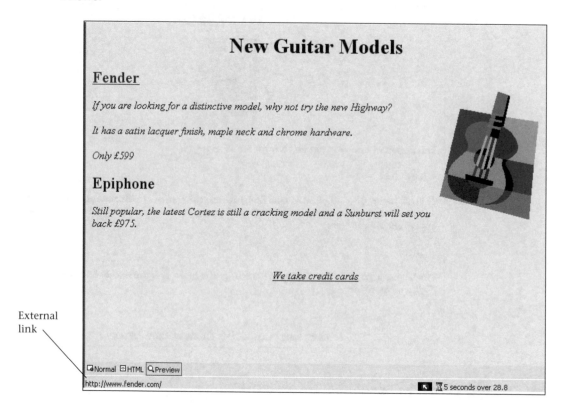

External link

Exercise 11 You are going to create some web pages for your dog kennel business.

1. Create a new document.

2. Insert the text file *Doggerel Kennels*.

3. Save the document as *kennel.htm* into the same folder as the text file.

4. Format the text Doggerel Kennels to Heading text.

5. Format the text The safe holiday home for pets as Subheading text.

6. Format the rest of the document as Body text.

7.   Right-align the heading.

8.   Centre the subheading.

9.   Insert the image *dog* and position it on the left of the page, just below the heading.

10.   Save these changes.

11.   Start a new document.

12.   Insert the text file *Travel*.

13.   Save the document as *directions.htm*.

14.   Format the text How to Find Doggerel Kennels as Heading text.

15.   Format the text From Exeter and From Dawlish as Subheading text.

16.   Format the rest of the text to Body text, italic.

17.   Centre both subheadings.

18.   Apply a yellow background colour to both pages.

19.   Save these changes.

20.   Now link *kennels.htm* to *directions.htm* using beautiful part of Devon as the link text.

21.   Add an external link from *directions.htm* to the Automobile Association website at www.theaa.com. Use From Exeter as the link text.

22.   Save these changes.

23.   Test both links in your browser.

Answer

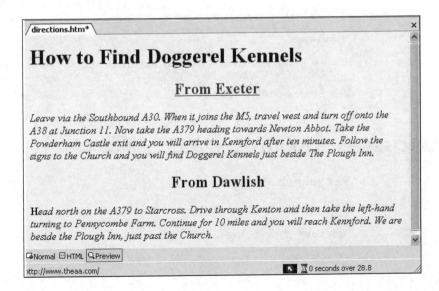

Exercise 12

1. Open *france.htm*.

2. You are going to link this to a travel agent page. Create a new page and add the following text:

   Go France Travel Agency (Heading-level text – large font size)

   We specialize in holidays in rural France (Subheading text)

   Phone us today on 020 445 37683 and we will create a tailor-made holiday for you (main Body text).

3. Save as *travel.htm*.

4. On the *france* page, select the text *The best time to visit* and use this as link text to link to the page *travel.htm*.

5. Save the amended page.

6. On the *France* page, link the text *Champagne* to the French Tourist Office website **www.francetourism.com**.

7. Test the links in your browser.

Answer

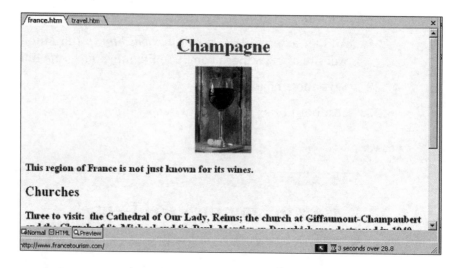

EXERCISES 13, 14 AND 15

Test your ability to:

◗ Insert an e-mail link

Assessment Objectives: 3c

Exercise 13 1. On the page *kennel.htm* you are going to add an e-mail link.

2. Enter the text from the Proprietor. after the words prices and facilities and apply the same formatting.

3. Use this new text to link the page to the e-mail address: info@doggerel_kennels.co.uk.

4. Save this amendment.

Answer

Exercise 14 1. On the page *music shop.htm* leave a clear line space and then add the following text below *Open 7 days a week*: Contact Dave for full details of our range.

2. Make sure this new text is formatted to Body text, left aligned.

3. Link the word Dave to the e-mail address dave@dontfret.co.uk.

4. Save this amendment.

Answer

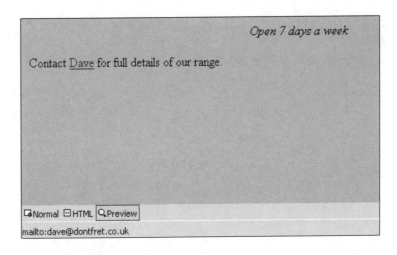

7

Exercise 15

1. Open the page *travel.htm*.

2. You are going to add an e-mail link to the travel agency. Add the following text below the phone number, leaving a clear line space:

   Contact our staff today.

3. Select the text and use it as the link to the e-mail address info@gofrance.co.uk.

4. Save this amendment to the page.

Answer

EXERCISES 16 AND 17

Test your ability to:

▶ Print web pages

▶ Print html source code

▶ Close a document

Assessment Objectives: 4a and 4b

Exercise 16   1.   Print a copy of *guitars.htm*.

2.   Print a copy of the HTML source code for this page.

3.   Close the document.

4.   Print a copy of *music shop.htm*.

5.   Print a copy of the HTML source code for this page.

6.   Close the document.

Answer

```
/ music shop.htm \ guitars.htm \
<meta name="GENERATOR" content="Microsoft FrontPage 5.0">
<meta name="ProgId" content="FrontPage.Editor.Document">
<meta http-equiv="Content-Type" content="text/html; charset=windows-1252">
<title>Don</title>
<style>
<!--
 li.MsoNormal
     {mso-style-parent:"";
     margin-bottom:.0001pt;
     font-size:12.0pt;
     font-family:Arial;
     margin-left:0cm; margin-right:0cm; margin-top:0cm}
-->
</style>
</head>

<body bgcolor="#FFCC66">

<h1 align="center">Don't Fret Guitars </h1>
<h2 align="center"> </h2>
<h2 align="center">
<img border="0" src="instruments.gif" width="178" height="191"></h2>
<h2>The best instruments money can buy </h2>
<h4><span style="font-weight: 400">If you are looking for a
<a href="guitars.htm">new guitar</a>, visit our shop in Brighton for the latest,
cheapest and best-looking models. </span></h4>
<h4 align="center"><span style="font-weight: 400; font-style: italic">Open 7
days a week </span></h4>
<h4><span style="font-weight: 400">Contact <a href="mailto:dave@dontfret.co.uk">
Dave</a> for full details of our range.</span></h4>
<p align="left"> </p>
<p> </p>
<p> </p>
<p> </p>
```

Exercise 17   1.   Print a copy of *kennel.htm*.

2.   Print a copy of the HTML source code for this page.

3.   Close the document.

4.   Print a copy of *destination.htm*.

5.   Print a copy of the HTML source code for this page.

6.   Close the document.

7

Answer

FULL ASSIGNMENTS – WEB PAGE CREATION

Exercise 18

Task 1

1. Rename the folder containing the file *indian recipes.htm* as *Curries*.

2. You have been asked to make a new page, about extra ingredients needed for some recipes. Create a new document and insert the text file *kitchen*.

3. Enter your name after the text **created by** and save the page as *kitchen.htm*.

Task 2

4. Format the page as follows:

   Text: IN THE KITCHEN as a Heading (large font size)

   Text: MASALAS, NATURAL YOGHURT and TAMARIND as Subheadings (medium font size)

   Format all other text as Body Text (small font size).

5. Ensure that all paragraphs are separated by a clear line space.

6. Format the heading to be centre aligned.

7. Underline the three subheadings.

8. Insert the image *spices* and position it below the MASALAS paragraph but above the subheading NATURAL YOGHURT.

9. Centre the image on the page.

10. Link this page to the *indian recipes.htm* page provided. Use the text main menu as the link text.

11. Check the page *kitchen.htm* for accuracy.

12. Save the page using the same name.

Task 3

13. You need to make changes to the Home Page *indian recipes.htm*.

    a) Add your name on the *indian recipes.htm* page after created by.

    b) Add a final sentence to the first paragraph: Find out what useful items you should always have in your kitchen.

    c) Add a link from this page to *kitchen.htm*. Use the text in your kitchen.

    d) Save the amended page *indian recipes.htm* with the same name.

Task 4

14. Apply a coloured background to the *indian recipes.htm* page.

15. You need an external link from the *indian recipes.htm* page to the various supermarkets mentioned. Use the text Waitrose in the first paragraph to create an external link to www.waitrose.com and then save this amendment.

16. Create an e-mail link in the *indian recipes.htm* page using your name as the link text. The e-mail address is info@goangoodies.com.

17. Save these amendments.

18. Load your pages into your browser and test the links.

19. Print a copy of each page.

20. Print copies of the HTML code used for each page.

21. Close all documents and exit from the application.

7

kitchen.htm | **Indian Recipes.htm***

INDIAN RECIPES FOR EVERYONE

This Website will show you how to cook the best Indian meals you will ever taste. Nowadays you can find appropriate ingredients for all the meals in UK supermarkets such as Sainsbury's, Waitrose and Tesco, so follow the instructions and start cooking. We cover three major categories, but will add to these as the site is developed. Find out what useful items you should always have in your kitchen.

TANDOORI

This word means 'oven' and the recipes are mainly from North India. Although it started with bread, this type of cooking now covers meat, fish and vegetables. Find out how to cook chicken, trout, naan and chapatti.

GOA

The west coast of India was colonized by the Portuguese and the cuisine relies heavily on coconut, lime juice and seafood. We will show you how to cook balchao, fish curry and pork vindaloo.

DESSERTS

You may have already discovered Indian ice-cream (kulfi), but you must also try gold-covered halwas, gulab jamum and Southern Indian rice puddings.

Page created by My Name.

IN THE KITCHEN

Here are three important items you will need for many of the recipes. There are ready-made alternatives but ideally make your own for the freshest and most authentic taste.

MASALAS

These are simply ground spice combinations which are required for different dishes. Most famous is Garam Masala which contains cardamom, cloves, mace, cinnamon, cumin, coriander, fennel, peppercorns and fenugreek.

NATURAL YOGHURT

To make your own, all you need do is bring whole milk to the boil and then cool it to 46–50 degrees C. Whisk in a couple of tablespoons of natural set whole milk yoghurt and then leave it to set for 6–8 hours.

TAMARIND

```
<html>

<head>
<meta http-equiv="Content-Language" content="en-gb">
<meta name="GENERATOR" content="Microsoft FrontPage 5.0">
<meta name="ProgId" content="FrontPage.Editor.Document">
<meta http-equiv="Content-Type" content="text/html; charset=windows-1252">
<title>IN THE KITCHEN</title>
</head>

<body>

<h1 align="center">IN THE KITCHEN </h1>
<h4>Here are three important items you will need for many of the recipes. There
are ready-made alternatives but ideally make your own for the freshest and most
authentic taste. </h4>
<h2><u>MASALAS </u></h2>
<h4>These are simply ground spice combinations which are required for different
dishes. Most famous is Garam Masala which contains cardamom, cloves, mace,
cinnamon, cumin, coriander, fennel, peppercorns and fenugreek. </h4>
<h4 align="center"><img border="0" src="spices.jpg" width="259" height="171"></h4>
<h2><u>NATURAL YOGHURT </u></h2>
<h4>To make your own, all you need do is bring whole milk to the boil and then
cool it to 46 - 50 degrees C. Whisk in a couple of tablespoons of natural set
whole milk yoghurt and then leave it to set for 6-8 hours. </h4>
<h2><u>TAMARIND </u></h2>
<h4>This is a sour fruit that imparts a specific flavour as well as colour to
curries and chutneys. You could substitute lemon juice but try to find it in
compressed blocks. These should be soaked in water for 2 hours and then sieved.
</h4>
<h4>Return to the <a href="Indian%20Recipes.htm">main menu</a></h4>
<h4>Page created by My Name</h4>

</body>
```

Exercise 19   You are working on a website advertising painting holidays.

Task 1

1. Rename the folder containing the files as *Painting*.

2. You are going to make a new page about the tutors. Create a new document and insert the text file *Staff*.

3. Add your name at the end of the text after Webmaster and save the file as *tutors.htm*.

Task 2

4. Format the page as follows:

    OUR TUTORS as Heading text (large font size)

    The names of the teachers as Subheading text (medium font size)

    The rest of the page as Body text (small font size, not bold).

5. Centre-align the main heading and 3 subheadings only.

6. Insert the image *paint* and position it on the right of the page, just below the heading.

7. You now need to link this new page to *painting.htm*. Use the text Home Page as the link text.

8. Save the amended page with the same file name.

9. Close *tutors.htm*.

Task 3

10. Open the Home Page *painting.htm* provided.

11. It should have a link to *tutors.htm*. Type the following text in the TEACH-ING paragraph, after the words *All our classes are run by qualified staff*: who are also professional painters. Add a link to the *tutors.htm* page using the text qualified staff as the link text.

12. Add an external link from the homepage to the painting magazine mentioned. Use the link text Leisure Painter and the address www.leisurepainter.co.uk.

13. Now create an e-mail link from this page. Use the text The Principal as the link text and the e-mail address enquiries@paintforpleasure.co.uk.

Task 4

14. Change the background colour of the homepage *painting.htm*.

15. Add your name after Webmaster.

16. Check for accuracy and save these changes.

17. Load the pages into your browser and test the links.

18. Print a copy of *painting.htm* from the browser.

19. Now print a copy showing the HTML code.

20. Print a copy of *tutors.htm* from the browser.

21. Print a copy showing the HTML code.

22. Close each document and exit the application.

PAINTING HOLIDAYS OVERSEAS

To capture the most beautiful light and scenery in the world, you really need to paint in Italy.

WHERE TO STAY

Our 1-week holidays will take you to Florence, Fiesole or Amalfi where you will stay in wonderful villas, eat fabulous local food and be shown how to improve your watercolour or oil painting techniques.

TEACHING

All our classes are run by qualified staff who are also professional painters.

BOOKING

We are keen to know how you found out about us. Please mention the source e.g. your local newspaper or Leisure Painter magazine, when you book your holiday. Book online by contacting The Principal.

OUR TUTORS

We have three resident tutors, one of whom will look after you on your painting holiday.

FRANK BONNER

Frank is well known for his oil paintings of trees, and has had many exhibits shown at the Royal Academy.

SHEILA WELLS

Sheila has been teaching for 30 years and still finds time to paint miniature flower pictures for which she is rightly famous.

DAVE INKSON

```
    font-size:12.0pt;
    font-family:Arial;
    margin-left:0cm; margin-right:0cm; margin-top:0cm}
-->
</style>
</head>

<body bgcolor="#FF9999">

<h1><span lang="EN-GB">PAINTING HOLIDAYS OVERSEAS</span></h1>
<h4><span lang="EN-GB"> </span><span style="font-weight: 400">To capture the
most beautiful light and scenery in the world, you really need to paint in
Italy. </span></h4>
<h2> WHERE TO STAY</h2>
<h4><span style="font-weight: 400">Our 1-week holidays will take you to
Florence, Fiesole or Amalfi where you will stay in
wonderful villas, eat fabulous local food and be shown how to improve your
watercolour or oil painting techniques.</span></h4>
<h2><span lang="EN-GB"> </span>TEACHING</h2>
<h4><span style="font-weight: 400">All our classes are run by
<a href="tutors.htm">qualified staff</a> who are also professional painters.</span></h4>
<h2> BOOKING</h2>
<h4><span style="font-weight: 400">We are keen to know how you found out about
us.  Please mention the source e.g. your local newspaper or
<a href="http://www.leisurepainter.co.uk">Leisure Painter</a> magazine, when you
book your holiday.  Book online by contacting
<a href="mailto:enquiries@paintforpleasure.co.uk">The Principal.</a></span></h4>
<h4> </h4>
<h4> </h4>
<h4><span style="font-weight: 400">Webmaster My Name</span></h4>
```

Exercise 20

Task 1

You are setting up a website advertising family-friendly places to stay.

1. Rename the folder containing the text file *menus* as *Hotels*.

2. You need a new page about children's menus. Create a new document and insert the text file *menus*.

3. Add your name at the bottom of the page after the text **For problems with this website contact**.

4. Save the page as *children.htm* into the *Hotels* folder.

Task 2

5. Format the new page as follows:

   CHILDREN'S MEALS as Heading text (large font size)

   THE MEALS, HOTEL A LA CARTE and **FOOD QUALITY** Subheading text (medium font size)

   The rest of the text as Body text (small font size, italic)

6. Centre the heading **CHILDREN'S MEALS**.

7. Insert the image *prize* onto the page. Left-align it below the first paragraph but above the text THE MEALS.

8. Create a link on this new page back to the Home Page *berkshire.htm* provided. Use the text Choose a hotel as the link text.

9. You need to add an external link from the menus page to the Food Standards Agency website. Use the text Food Standards Agency on the *children.htm* page to link it to www.food.gov.uk.

10. Save *children.htm*.

Task 3

11. On *berkshire.htm* add your name at the bottom of the page after the text For problems with this website contact.

12. This page should have a link to *children.htm*. Use the text young children in the first paragraph as the link.

13. Save the amended page.

14. Now add an e-mail link to the *berkshire.htm* page. Use the text Jim as the link text and link it to jim@chequers_hotels.co.uk.

15. Save the amended page after checking for accuracy.

Task 4

16. Apply a different background colour to *berkshire.htm*.

17. Load your pages into your browser and test the links.

18. Print a copy of each page.

19. Print a copy of the HTML code used for each page.

20. Close the pages and exit the application.

7

Answer 20a – image in place

CHILDREN'S MEALS

If you are afraid your kids won't like the food in some of the hotels, don't worry.

Hotels with children's menus are marked with our Prize symbol.

THE MEALS

You will be offered a range of tasty foods such as chicken nuggets, sausages and chips, burgers or spaghetti Bolognese.

All the meals include a fruit drink and ice-cream and are very good value.

HOTEL A LA CARTE

Answer 20b

BERKSHIRE HOTELS

There are two marvellous hotels in this county where you can happily take your <u>*young children*</u> *and have a wonderful holiday.*

THE CHEQUERS HOTEL

Situated in Castle Road, Hungerford, this is the perfect place for kids to let off steam as there is a bouncy castle and swings installed in the large garden. Unfussy but attentive staff will look after you and some excellent food is available as Annie is a Cordon Bleu chef.

Book your rooms with <u>*Jim*</u>.

SWALLOW HOTEL

This is in Low Road, Reading and is an imposing Victorian building with wonderful views of the Downs. There is a small heated pool with a shallow end, and you can play mini-golf or croquet on the vast lawn.

Book your family room with Denise.

Back to Main List of entries.

For problems with this website contact My Name

```
berkshire.htm
<html>

<head>
<meta http-equiv="Content-Language" content="en-gb">
<meta name="GENERATOR" content="Microsoft FrontPage 5.0">
<meta name="ProgId" content="FrontPage.Editor.Document">
<meta http-equiv="Content-Type" content="text/html; charset=windows-1252">
<title>New Page 1</title>
</head>

<body bgcolor="#00FF00">

<h1>BERKSHIRE HOTELS</h1>
<h3><i>There are two marvellous hotels in this county where you can happily take
your <a href="children.htm">young children</a> and have a wonderful holiday.</i></h3>
<h2>THE CHEQUERS HOTEL</h2>
<h3><i>Situated in Castle Road, Hungerford, this is the perfect place for kids
to let off steam as there is a bouncy castle and swings installed in the large
garden.  Unfussy but attentive staff will look after you and some excellent
food is available as Annie is a Cordon Bleu chef.</i></h3>
<h3><i>Book your rooms with <a href="mailto:jim@chequers_hotels.co.uk">Jim</a>.</i></h3>
<h2>SWALLOW HOTEL</h2>
<h3><i>This is in Low Road, Reading and is an imposing Victorian building with
wonderful views of the Downs.  There is a small heated pool with a shallow
end, and you can play mini-golf or croquet on the vast lawn.</i></h3>
<h3><i>Book your family room with Denise.</i></h3>
<h3><i>Back to Main List of entries.</i></h3>
<h3><i>For problems with this website contact My Name</i></h3>

</body>

</html>
```

7

Online communication

For this unit you will be asked to send and receive e-mails including attached files, search the World Wide Web and save and print information that you find.

EXERCISES 1, 2 AND 3

Test your ability to:

◗ Use appropriate software

◗ Create a new message

◗ Send a message

◗ Copy a message

Assessment Objectives: 1a, 3i and 3j

Exercise 1 **1.** Open your e-mail system.

2. Compose a new message as follows:

Send it to peter@pearsoned-ema.com

Copy it to yourself

Subject of message: Help Required

Message: Please could you help me sort out my printing problems. Although my machine has a colour cartridge, it is only printing in black and white. Many thanks.

End the message with your name.

3. Send the message.

Exercise 2 1. Compose a new message as follows:

Send it to peter@pearsoned-ema.com

Copy it to yourself.

Subject of message: Using e-mail

Message: I think I have finally sorted out the difference between replying to and forwarding e-mails. Thank you for your help in this matter.

End the message with your name.

2. Send the message.

Exercise 3 1. Compose a new message as follows:

Send it to yourself

Subject of message: Receiving Mail

Message: Sending this to my own e-mail address will ensure I receive a message. I will then be able to open and read it.

End the message with your name.

2. Send the message.

Answer

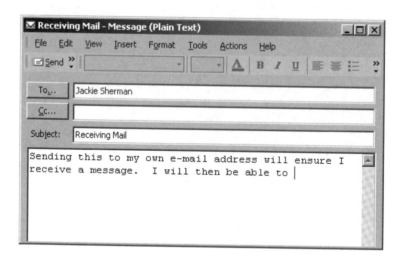

Test your ability to:

- ◗ Access an incoming message
- ◗ Store an e-mail address
- ◗ Reply to a message
- ◗ Forward a message

Assessment Objectives: 3a, 3d, 3g and 3h

Exercise 4

1. Access the copied message you should receive with the subject: Help Required.

2. Reply to the message. The message content should be: I have sorted out the problem myself. Thanks.

3. End the message with your name and then send it.

4. You are going to forward the message you received to mary@pearsoned-ema.com. Before sending it, add the following: As you see, I seem to have sorted out the printer problem.

5. You have been given a new e-mail address by a friend. Add it to your address book. Her name is Fran White and her address is f.white21@yahoo.co.uk.

Exercise 5

1. Access the copy you received with the subject Using e-mail.

2. Reply to this message with the following content: I should say that I still find Reply and Reply All rather confusing.

3. End the message with your name and then send it.

4. You are going to forward the message to mary@pearsoned-ema.com. Before sending, add the following: Does replying confuse you as well?

5. You have been given a new e-mail address by a friend. Add it to your address book. His name is Stewart Bolder and his address is bolders@hotmail.com.

8

Answer   adding address

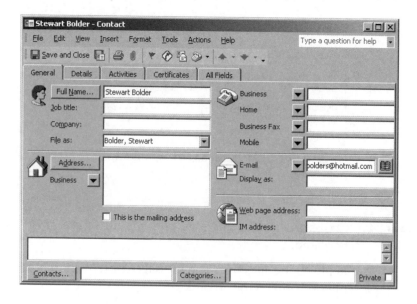

Exercise 6   1. Open the message you sent to yourself entitled Receiving Mail.

2. Prepare a reply with the added text: This was a successful operation.

3. Forward a copy of the message to peter@pearsoned-ema.com with the added text: I hope this forwarded message arrives safely.

4. Finally, add the e-mail address of the Department for Education and Skills: info@dfes.gov.uk to your address book.

Answer   replying

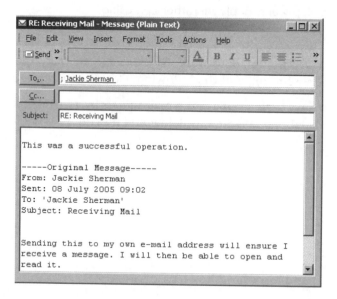

Test your ability to:

◗ Attach a file to an e-mail message

◗ Delete an e-mail message

◗ (You will also need to have access to the files mentioned. They are on the accompanying CD-ROM. You could create and save the text documents using a text editor or word processing application and attach any image saved on your computer, if you prefer.)

Assessment Objectives: 3c and 3k

Exercise 7

1. Store the address of Peter Blake, peter@pearsoned-ema.com, in your address book.

2. Create a new e-mail message addressed to peter@pearsoned-ema.com and copy it to yourself.

3. The subject of the message is **Buses**.

4. Type the following message: **Here are the times of the buses that you wanted.**

5. Sign the message with your name.

6. [If creating your own documents: Open a text editing or word processing program and start a new document. Type the following: **Gloucester to London – 10.00 or 12.30**. Save the document as *Bus times*.

7. Now create a second document. Type the words **Stour River** and save the document as *fishing*.

8. Close both documents and return to your message.]

9. Attach the document *Bus times* to your message.

10. Send the message.

11. Delete the message with the subject **Help Required** that you copied to yourself and which should have appeared in your Inbox.

8

Answer

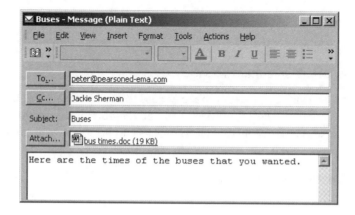

Exercise 8

1. Create a new message addressed to yourself.

2. It should have the subject Buses from Gloucester.

3. Message content: This is a copy of the bus times I sent Peter.

4. Attach the document *bus times*.

5. Send the message.

6. Create a second message addressed to yourself.

7. It should have the subject Going Fishing.

8. Message content: I must remember where we are fishing next week.

9. Attach the file *fishing*.

10. Send the message.

11. Store the address of Mary Jones, mary@pearsoned-ema.com, in your address book.

12. Delete the copy of the message you sent yourself about using e-mail that should have arrived in your Inbox.

Exercise 9

1. Create a new message addressed to yourself.

2. It should have the subject New Café.

3. Message content: We are setting up a café in town and want to advertise it. Here is a picture that might do for the ad.

4. Attach the image file *cake* (on the CD).

5. Send the message.

6. Delete the copy that will be saved in your Sent folder.

Answer

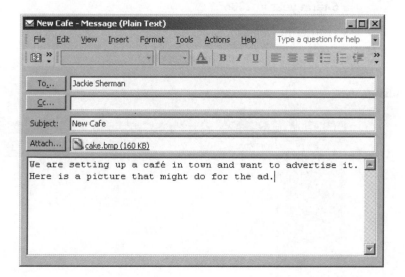

EXERCISES 10, 11 AND 12

Test your ability to:

- Access an attachment
- Recall a stored e-mail address
- Store an attachment
- Print a message and attachment

Assessment Objectives: 3b, 3e, 3f and 3l

Exercise 10 1. Access the message New Café that you sent yourself.

2. Open the attached image file *cake*.

3. Print a copy of the image.

4. Save the attachment onto your computer outside your e-mail system.

5. Print a copy of the e-mail message displaying all headers (To, From, Date etc.).

6. Compose a new message to the Department for Education and Skills, recalling their e-mail address from your address book.

7. Subject: Information on School Terms.

8

8. Message Content: Please would you tell me which counties have opted for a 6-term year in 2006.

9. Sign the message.

10. Close the message without saving.

Answer

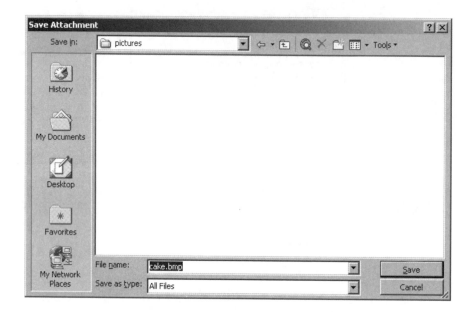

Exercise 11

1. Access the message **Buses** that you copied to yourself.

2. Open the attached file *Bus times*.

3. Save the file onto your computer outside your e-mail system. (If you have stored the original in the same location, you may be asked to save it with a different name or to overwrite the original file.)

4. Print a copy of the file *Bus times*.

5. Print a copy of the e-mail message, making sure all headers (To, From, Date etc.) are displayed.

6. Compose a new message to Peter at Pearson, recalling his e-mail address from your address book.

7. The subject of the message: **Meeting**.

8. The content of the message: I hope you can catch the early bus.

9. Sign the message and send it.

Exercise 12 1. Access the message Going Fishing that you sent yourself.

2. Save the attached file *fishing* onto your computer outside your e-mail system.

3. Print a copy of the file.

4. Print a copy of the e-mail message, displaying all headers.

5. Compose a new message to Mary at Pearson, recalling her address from your address book.

6. Subject: Away Next Week.

7. Message content: Peter and I will be on a fishing trip next week.

8. Sign and send the message.

EXERCISES 13, 14 AND 15

Test your ability to:

- Use appropriate software
- Access specific web pages
- Navigate the Web using hyperlinks
- Use a local search facility
- Locate web pages containing required data
- Use a general web search engine
- Store a web address (URL)

Assessment Objectives: 1a, 2a, 2b, 2c, 2d, 2e and 2g

Exercise 13 1. Open your browser and connect to the Internet.

2. Visit the Pearson homepage at **www.pearsoned.com**.

3. Open a new page by clicking a hyperlink, e.g. Shop, About Us or Contact.

4. View the contents of the page.

5. Return to the homepage.

6. Now visit the search engine Google at **www.google.co.uk**.

7. Search for websites on poisonous plants.

8. Visit any site and use the local search facilities to find information about one poisonous plant, e.g. Yew.

9. Store the URL of this page – if you want to, create a *plants* folder in which to store it.

Answer 13a

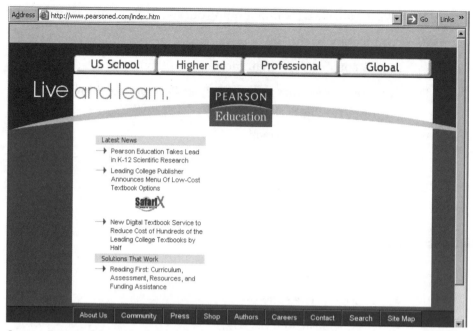

Source: Pearson Education homepage: http://www.pearsoned.com/index.htm. Pearson Education, Inc. Reprinted by permission of Pearson Education, Inc., Upper Saddle River, New Jersey.

Answer 13b

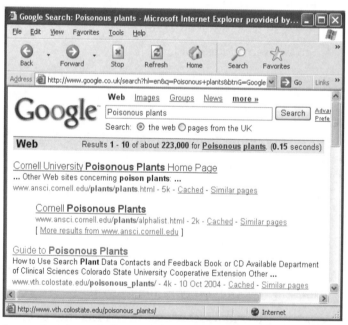

Source: Search results from google.com: http://www.google.co.uk/search?hl=en&q=Poisonous+plants&btnG=Google. Google is a trademark of Google, Inc. Reprinted by permission.

Answer 13c

Source: From the Guide to Poisonous Plants website: http://www.vth.colostate.
edu/poisonous_plants/report/plant_report2.cfm. Reprinted by permission of
A. P. Knight, Department of Clinical Sciences, Colorado State University.

Answer 13d

Exercise 14
1. Visit the search engine website www.gigablast.com.

2. Use it to find some information about travelling through the Channel Tunnel, e.g. on Eurostar trains.

3. Visit some of the websites displayed in the search list and bookmark one page that has relevant information.

4. Use the local search facility to find out fares or timetables for a journey on a specific date.

Answer

Source: From the Rail Europe website: http://www.raileurope.com/us/rail/eurostar/.
Reprinted by permission of Rail Europe Group.

Exercise 15   1.   Visit the auction website www.ebay.co.uk.

2.   Use their index to locate the section offering Musical Instruments for sale.

3.   Follow the link to Harmonicas/Keyboard/Pianos and click on Pianos.

4.   On the page that opens, check how many items are currently for sale.

5.   Now visit the search engine site www.altavista.com and look for information on any musical instrument museums in the UK.

6.   Bookmark the page of an interesting museum you find.

Answer   15a

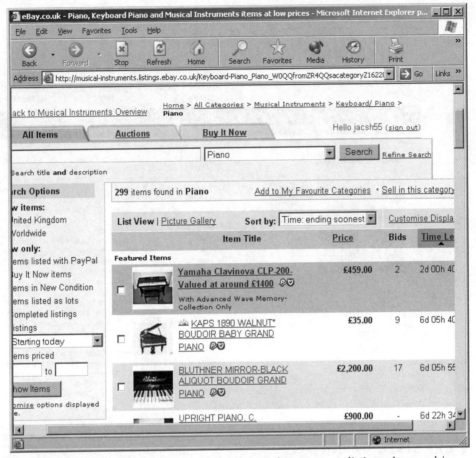

Source: Search results from e-bay.com: http://musical-instruments.listings.ebay.co.uk/
Keyboard-Piano_W0QQfromZR4QQscategoryZ16220QQsalicZ3. These materials have
been reproduced with the permission of eBay Inc. Copyright © eBay Inc. All rights
reserved.

Answer 15b

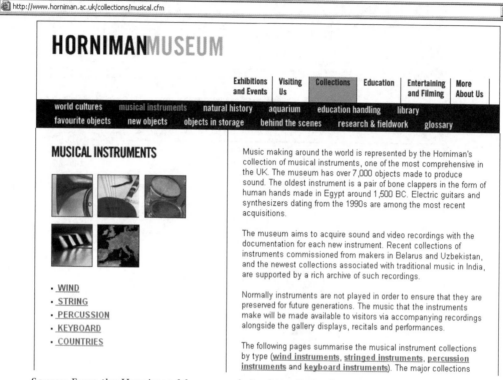

Source: From the Horniman Museum website: http://www.horniman.ac.uk/collections/
musical.php. Reprinted by permission of The Horniman Museum, London.

EXERCISES 16 AND 17

Test your ability to:

▶ Save data from a web page

▶ Print a web page

Assessment Objectives: 2f and 2h

Exercise 16   You are going to visit the BBC weather website and find out what the weather will be like in your nearest large town over the next few days.

1. Go to www.bbc.co.uk.

2. Find the weather link on the homepage, e.g. *Where I live* or use the index.

3. In the *change location* box, enter the name of your nearest large town.

4. With the correct town now showing, select the Local 5-day forecast link and view the details.

5. Print a copy of the page.

6. Save an image from the page, e.g. of sun or clouds etc., onto your computer.

Answer 16a

Source: From the BBC website: http://www.bbc.co.uk

Answer 16b

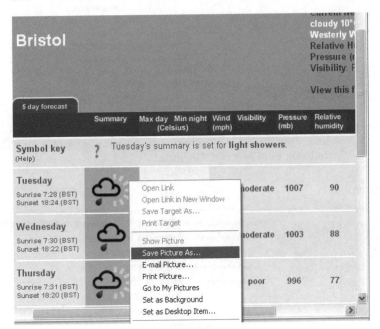

Source: From the BBC website: http://www.bbc.co.uk

Exercise 17   You are going to find out some information about voluntary work.

1. Visit the website **www.volwork.org.uk**.

2. Use the index to go to the page on Volunteers and then find the page of examples of volunteers who have registered.

3. Print a copy of the page showing the chart.

4. Save the image of the chart separately onto your computer.

Answer 17a

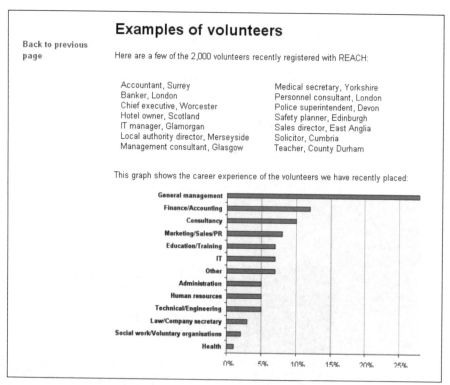

Source: From the REACH website: http://www.reach-online.org.uk. Reprinted by permission of REACH Volunteering.

Answer 17b

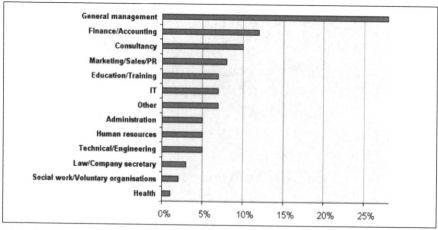

Source: From the REACH website: http://www.reach-online.org.uk. Reprinted by permission of REACH Volunteering.

[For these exercises, you will need to receive an e-mail. If a tutor or colleague cannot send them to you, send them to yourself.]

Exercise 18

You need to receive the following e-mail:

From: jamescox@pearsoned-ema.com

Subject: Becoming a School Governor

Attachment: swim.jpg (on accompanying CD-ROM)

Message: Now you have agreed to become a governor and you and Sally will take swimming classes for us, you may like to keep a copy of this image to add to your documents.

James Cox
Headteacher

Task 1

1. Open your Inbox and read the message from James Cox entitled Becoming a School Governor.

2. Scan the attachment *swim.jpg* for viruses.

3. Save the attachment outside your mailbox.

4. Reply to James with the following message: Many thanks for the picture. I have sent a copy to Sally.

5. Add your name at the end of the message and then send it, making sure a copy will be saved in your Sent folder.

Task 2

6. You are going to forward the message Becoming a School Governor and its attachment to Sally@pearsoned-ema.com. Enter the text: This is the picture you wanted. Add your name at the end of the message.

7. Forward the message and ensure a copy is saved in your Sent folder.

8. Delete the original message Becoming a School Governor.

9. Print a copy of your Inbox, e.g. as a screen print, making sure your name is visible somewhere on the page.

8

Task 3

10. Add the following contact to your address book:

Name: James Cox, Headteacher
e-mail address: jamescox@pearsoned-ema.com

11. Produce a printout of these details.

12. Prepare a new e-mail message to James Cox. Recall his address from your address book.

13. Give the message the subject heading New for Governors.

Use the following message text: I thought you would like to see an image we can use for our School Governor reports.

14. Copy the message to steven@pearsoned-ema.com.

15. Locate and attach the image file *governor.gif*.

16. Send the message, making sure a copy is saved in your sent folder.

17. Locate and print a copy of the messages you have sent, making sure header details and evidence of any attachments are visible.

Your reply to the original message
Your forwarded message
The new message titled: New for Governors

18. Close your e-mail system.

Task 4

19. Use a Web-based search engine to search for pages on the journalist *Joan Sallis* who writes about school governors. Follow links to a web page providing information about her or a sample of one of her articles or books.

20. Bookmark the page.

21. Print a copy of the first page displaying the information.

22. You now need to find information on the Dfes advice for governors. Access the Dfes website at **www.dfes.gov.uk**. Follow links to the School Governors website.

23. Bookmark the page.

24. Print a copy of the entire web page.

25. Save only the *What's New?* image (or an alternative image) that is visible on the page as *new.gif*.

26. Exit the browser.

27. Take a screen print of the folder containing the two image files *new.gif* and *swim.jpg*.

Answer 18a – new message

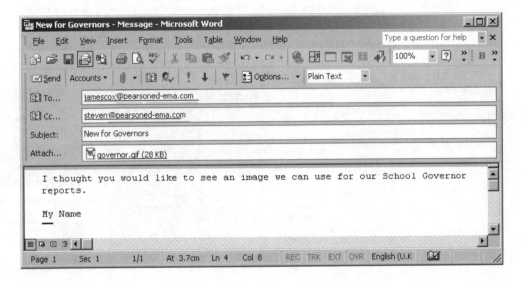

Answer 18b – step 21

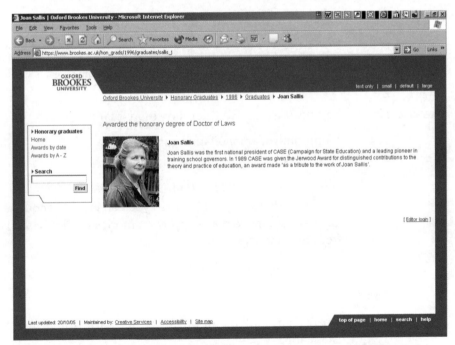

Source: From the Oxford Brookes University website: https://www.brookes.ac.uk/hon_grads/1996/graduates/sallis_j . Reprinted by permission of Oxford Brookes University and Joan Sallis.

Answer 18c – web page and saving image

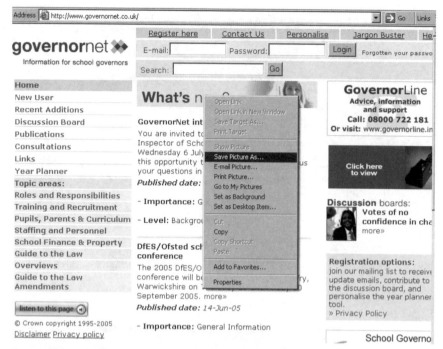

Source: From the Governornet website: http://www.governornet.co.uk. Crown copyright material is reproduced under Class Licence Number CO1W0000039 with the permission of the Controller of HMSO and the Queen's Printer for Scotland.

Exercise 19   You need to receive the following e-mail:

From: tim@pearsoned-ema.com

Subject: Studying a Language

Attachment: *pisa.bmp* (on accompanying CD-ROM)

Message: There are many places you can learn a language. I learned Italian last year and have many happy memories of Pisa. Here is a picture I took from the language school.

Tim

Task 1

1.   Open your mailbox and read the message from Tim entitled Studying a Language.

2.   Scan the attached file *pisa.bmp* for viruses.

3.   Save the file outside your mailbox.

4.   Prepare a reply to Tim with the following message: I like the picture, but I think I prefer to study Spanish.

5. Add your name at the end of the message.

6. Send the reply, making sure a copy is saved in your Sent folder.

Task 2

7. Prepare to forward the message Studying a Language and its attachment to sally@pearsoned-ema.com, adding the following text: Here is a message and picture from Tim. I think I would prefer to study Spanish. Would you like to come to a class with me?

8. Add your name at the end of the message.

9. Forward the message, making sure a copy is saved in your Sent folder.

10. Delete the original message: Studying a Language.

11. Print the contents of your Inbox.

Task 3

12. Add Tim's e-mail address to your address book. His name is Tim Green and his address is tim@pearsoned-ema.com.

13. Print this address book entry, first adding your name to the page.

14. Now prepare a new e-mail to go to Tim. Recall his address from your address book.

15. Give the message the title Spain Here I come.

16. Use the following message text: You can see from the attached picture that Sally and I have booked our places and are ready to start soon.

17. Locate and attach the image file *spain.gif*.

18. Add your name at the end of the message.

19. Make sure a copy of the message is sent to Sally at sally@pearsoned-ema.com.

20. Send the message and attachment, ensuring a copy is saved into your Sent folder.

21. Print out all messages that you have sent:

    your reply
    your forwarded message
    your new message.

    Ensure all headers and evidence of attachments are displayed.

22. Exit your e-mail system.

8

Task 4

23. You must now find some information on the Alhambra Palace in Granada, Spain as you want to visit one day. Use a web-based search engine to search for pages providing information on the palace.

24. Follow links to a specific page of information and bookmark it.

25. Print a copy of the page containing the information.

26. You must now find information on Spanish courses. Visit the website www.learndirect.co.uk and use the index to find their courses information and then details of Spanish courses.

27. Follow links to *Fun With Spanish – Beginner*.

28. In the bottom right-hand corner of the page locate and save a picture of a blue tick (or alternative picture) as *tick.gif*.

29. Print a copy of the entire web page.

30. Bookmark the page.

31. Exit your browser.

32. Take a screen print of the computer folder containing the two image files *tick.gif* and *pisa.bmp*.

Answer 19a – contact in address book

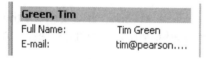

Answer 19b – details of Alhambra

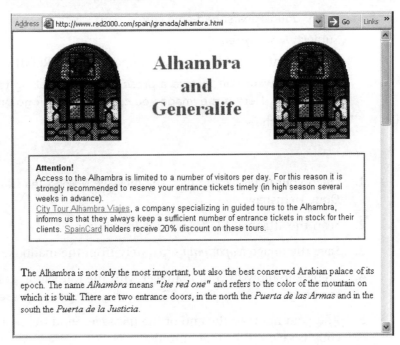

Source: From the All About Spain website: http://www.red2000.com/spain/granada/alhambra.html.

Answer 19c – Spanish course page

Source: From the LearnDirect website: http://catalogue.learndirect.co.uk/courses/100972EH017/?view=Ecommerce. Reprinted by permission of Ufi Ltd.

Exercise 20   You need to receive the following e-mail:

From: doug@pearsoned-ema.com

Subject: Making Tea

Attachment: *teapot.bmp* (on accompanying CD-ROM)

Message: I want you to give a presentation on making tea to our visitors next month. Here is the image you can use as the logo on your slides.

Doug Hernshaw

Task 1

1. Open your mailbox and read the message Making Tea from your manager, Doug Hernshaw.

2. Scan the attached file *teapot.bmp* for viruses.

3. Save the image *teapot.bmp* separately from the mailbox.

4. Prepare to reply to your manager with the following message: Thanks for the image. I have made sure Dawn will add it to the presentation.

5. Add your name to the end of the message. Send the reply, making sure a copy is saved in your Sent folder.

Task 2

6. Prepare to forward the message Making Tea and its attachment to your secretary dawn@pearsoned-ema.com, adding the following text: Please find attached the image we need to add to our slideshow on tea making.

7. Add your name to the end of the message and then send it. Make sure a copy is saved in your Sent folder.

8. Delete the original message Making Tea.

9. Print the contents of your Inbox.

Task 3

10. Add your manager's e-mail address to your address book. His details are: Name: Doug Hernshaw, Manager
e-mail: doug@pearsoned-ema.com

11. Print a copy of the entry.

12. Prepare a new e-mail message to your manager Doug Hernshaw using the address recalled from your address book.

13. Give the message the subject Tea Ceremony and use the following message: This is a picture we can add to the presentation.

14. Locate and attach the image file *ceremony.jpg*.

15. Make sure a copy will be sent to your secretary Dawn at dawn@pearsoned-ema.com.

16. Check your message for errors, make sure a copy is saved in your Sent folder and then send the message and attachment.

17. Print a copy of the messages you have sent, ensuring headers and attachments are visible:

   your reply
   your forwarded message
   your new message

18. Exit the e-mail system.

Task 4

19. You must now find out about Earl Grey tea for your presentation. Use a web-based search engine to find a page describing this type of tea.

20. Bookmark the page.

21. Print one copy of the information.

22. Your manager wants some images added to the presentation. You know you can find these on the Tea Council website. Go to www.teacouncil.co.uk and use the index to visit the Tea4health site listed. Here, follow links to the Tea Chart.

23. Save a picture of just the chart as *chart.jpg*.

24. Bookmark the page.

25. Print a copy of the entire page.

26. Take a screen print showing the contents of the folder containing the saved image files *chart.jpg* and *teapot.bmp*.

27. Exit the software securely.

8

Answer   20a – detail of Earl Grey tea

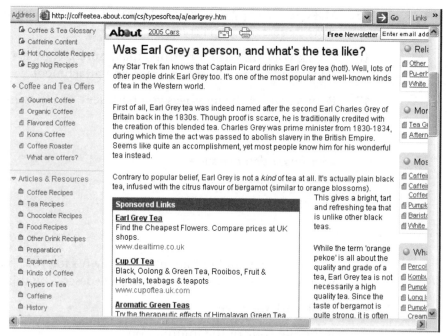

Source: From the About.com website: http://coffeetea.about.com/cs/typesoftea/a/earlgrey.htm.

Answer   20b – tea chart web page

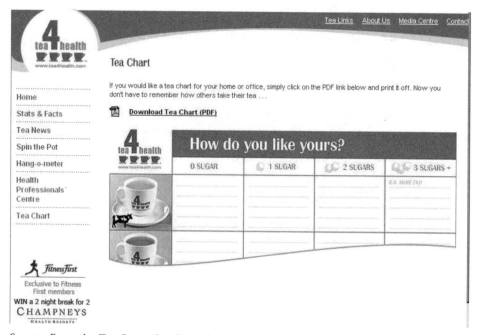

Source: From the Tea Council website: http://www.tea.co.uk. Courtesy of The Tea Council Ltd.

Answer   20c – saved image files

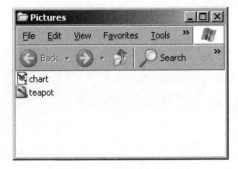

8

Index